365
ELEPHANTS

CLD21380

This edition published in 1999 for Colour Library Direct, Godalming
Business Centre, Woolsack Way, Godalming, Surrey, GU7 1XW

© 1999 Rebo International b.v.

text: Francisca Fröhlich
illustrations: Christl Vogl
translation: First Edition Translators, Cambridge
editor: Deborah Fox
production: TextCase, The Netherlands
cover design: Ton Wienbelt, The Netherlands

ISBN 1-84100-236-4

365 ELEPHANTS

Bedtime Stories for every day of the year

Colour
Library
Direct

Ollie the little elephant

Ollie the little elephant was the happiest animal in the forest. He was always having fun. He trumpeted different tunes all day long with a huge smile on his face. All the other animals were pleased when they saw Ollie. "Come and play with us," they cried. Ollie grinned from ear to ear. He stood up straight, stretched out his trunk, took a deep breath and blew, "Tarantara. Tarantara!"

Sad Ollie

It was very quiet in the wood, which was strange as Ollie was always making a noise. The bees were buzzing and the butterflies fluttered their wings, but why wasn't Ollie trumpeting any tunes? Where was he?
Ollie was sitting on a tree stump. Huge tears rolled down his cheeks, along his trunk and on to the grass. Bella Butterfly was worried about him.
"Ollie, whatever's the matter? Why are you crying?" she asked. Ollie sniffed and carried on crying. With a flutter of her wings, she jumped on the end of his trunk and then she blew. What a peculiar sound she made, nothing like Ollie's trumpeting at all. She blew again. Ollie chuckled. He would have to show her how it was done!

An elephant for a friend

Ollie had lots and lots of friends – Bella Butterfly, Sebastian Squirrel, Bertie Bear, Spike the hedgehog, Tommy Tortoise and Rachel Rabbit – but his best friend was Morris Mouse.

"You know you're my best friend," Ollie said one day to Morris, "but I'm always afraid of playing with you. You're so small and I'm so big and fat."

"Oh, don't worry about that Ollie. I'll squeak if you hurt me!" Morris answered bravely. "It's a shame you're not an elephant. Then we could tramp through the forest together."

"But we tramp through the forest together anyway, don't we?" said Morris.

"I know," agreed Ollie, "but it would still be nice to have another elephant for a friend!"

4 January

Looking for a friend

Ollie decided to look for an elephant friend, but he didn't know how to go about it.
"It's not so difficult," said Sebastian Squirrel. "Elephants are so big. We'll easily find one."
"I think I'm the only elephant around here," said Ollie sadly.
"No you're not," said Sebastian. "I saw a herd of elephants at the lake yesterday. They were having great fun. They were up to their knees in water and spraying their backs with their trunks." Ollie got excited.
"Then they began to spray each other," laughed Sebastian.
"What a lot of splashing. It was like bath-time at the zoo!"
"Oooh! Really?" cried Ollie. "I think I'll go and take a look. They could still be there!"

5 January

Splish splash splosh!

Splish splash
In the bath.
Splish splosh
Lovely wash!

Splish splash
Nearly done.
Splish splosh
Bathtime's fun!

A hundred elephants!

Sebastian Squirrel jumped from tree to tree, leading Ollie through the forest to the lake. As they got closer, there were fewer trees and the sun shone down on Ollie's smooth, round head.
"Phew, isn't it warm?" panted Ollie, "I wish we would reach the lake and then I could just throw myself in."
"We're nearly there!" cried Sebastian Squirrel. "Look!"
Ollie couldn't believe his eyes. He could see the cool, blue water of the lake ... and at least a hundred elephants!

7 January

Elephants are always grey

That evening, Ollie told Morris Mouse all about the elephants at the lake.
"And do you know what Morris? They're all grey!" said Ollie.
"Well, yes, elephants are supposed to be grey," answered Morris. "Mice can be white, black or brown. But elephants are always grey."
"Yes, but I'd like to see different coloured elephants, even spotted elephants!" cried Ollie.
"They only exist in your dreams," laughed Morris.
"Then I'd better go to sleep quickly!" Ollie closed his eyes and drifted off to sleep.

13

Dreamland

Ollie, Ollie, sweetly dreaming,
Elves will take you, starlight
   gleaming,
Over mountains, rivers
   streaming,
To the place you wish to be.

Dreamland is a happy place,
A smile on every jolly face.
Nobody is dull and grey,
Lots of colours, bright as day.

A purple bear

That night, Ollie fell into a deep, deep sleep. He dreamt about a beautiful place, far, far away. An elf had brought him there. When he arrived, Ollie couldn't believe his eyes. There were beautiful colours everywhere. He saw a bear. Not a brown bear, a grey or black bear, or even a white bear. But a purple bear with a pink nose! "Oh, you look amazing," shouted Ollie. "I am beautiful," answered the purple bear with a huge smile on his face. "All the animals here are beautiful. But I am the most beautiful of all!"

10 January

Come with me

Ollie was fascinated by the beautiful purple bear.

"Come with me," called the bear. "Let me show you how lovely it is here."

"Dreamland is the loveliest land in the world," said Morris Mouse.

"Hey, I didn't know you were here too," cried Ollie with surprise.

"Did you really think I would let you go on such an exciting journey without me?" said Morris. "I want to have an adventure too! Guess what I just saw? A purple giraffe with yellow suns all over him, and a jet-black parrot with red hearts on its wings. There was a zebra, but it didn't have ordinary black and white stripes. Oh no, it had red, white and blue stripes. It was amazing!"

15

11 January

A train of elephants

The purple bear showed Ollie and Morris round Dreamland. "Dreamland is so big," he said, "that if you want to see it all we must take the train." Then he clapped his chubby paws three times. "Ta-ran-ta-ra, ta-ran-ta-ree. Take me where I want to be!" he cried. Ollie and Morris then heard the rumble of a train approaching. They looked round. Trundling from a large pink cloud they saw the most peculiar train they had ever seen. Ollie and Morris rubbed their eyes in amazement. It wasn't the sort of train you would see every day. It was an elephant train! The engine was a green and yellow elephant with pink smoke coming out of his trunk. And all the wagons were elephants too, all different colours, just like a rainbow.

12 January

Together in the train

"Hurrah!" cried Ollie. "We're going on the train."
The purple bear, Morris and Ollie each jumped on to a
different wagon of the train. Then they set off on
their journey through Dreamland.
"Do you know what the best thing about this place is?"
asked the purple bear. "All the animals can choose what
colour they want to be. That's why the giraffe is purple
with yellow suns. He chose his favourite colours."

13 January

Animals in every colour

"Toot toot," sounded the elephant engine. The train
trundled through Dreamland.
"Look, there's a pink giraffe!" shouted the purple bear.
Ollie and Morris looked up and, peering over the top of the
palm trees, they saw the long pink neck of the giraffe.
"And look, there's Puss-puss. She's red and yellow today!"
laughed the bear. They rode on for hours and hours and, after
a while, Ollie got a little bit bored looking at all the different
colours. But he was too polite to say anything.

17

14 January

The animal painter

After a long, long time, the train began to slow down.
It squeaked, huffed and puffed, and finally stopped.
"Here we are!" said the purple bear happily. "This is where
the animal painter lives."
Ollie and Morris had seen lots and lots of animals in
Dreamland in a variety of colours.
"You mean that someone paints all the animals?" asked Ollie.
"Of course," answered the bear. "Which colour do you want to be?"

15 January

Choose a colour

Choose a colour by yourself,
Red or violet, green or blue,
Take a paintpot from the shelf,
Pick the one that shines like new.

Choose a colour, dark or light,
Black or pink, brown or grey,
Choose a colour, nice and bright,
One to make you smile all day.

Mr Paintpot

When Ollie and Morris arrived at the animal painter's
house, he greeted them.
"Hello," he said, "my name is Mr Paintpot. I can see
you both need a bit of colour to brighten you up."
"Hello, I'm Morris and this is Ollie," said Morris.
Ollie felt a little bit shy.
"Ollie and Morris would like to be painted beautiful
colours," said the purple bear.
"Yes, I'd really like to be red," cried Morris.
"And I want to be ... purple," whispered Ollie.

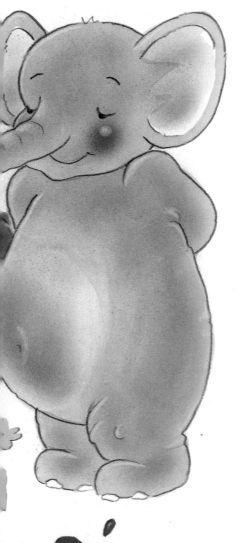

Friends

Ollie and Morris were looking forward to being painted.
"Are you two friends?" asked Mr Paintpot with a big smile.
Ollie and Morris nodded. "Then I'm afraid I can't possibly
paint you red and purple," said Mr Paintpot.
"But I thought we could choose the colours for ourselves?"
said Ollie.
"Yes, you can," answered Mr Paintpot, "but you"ll have to
choose colours that go together. Red and purple don't go
together very well. You couldn't be seen next to each other.
It would look too ugly!"

Choosing together

Ollie and Morris had to choose two colours that worked well together.
Only then would Mr Paintpot paint them.
"Which colour would you really like to be?"
Ollie asked his friend Morris.
"I would like to be red, bright red," answered Morris.
"I know, but Mr Paintpot doesn't think red goes with purple,"
Ollie sighed.
"Well, we are friends, aren't we?" said Morris. "So we should be able
to choose two colours that match!"

19 January

No arguments

Mr Paintpot, the animal painter, waited patiently for the two friends to
come to a decision. Ollie and Morris didn't want to start an argument.
"Red and yellow are nice," said Morris.
"I don't want to be yellow!" cried Ollie. "How about purple and orange?"
Morris really wanted to be bright red, but he thought about being
orange. "Okay," he said, "I suppose orange is close to red. I'll try orange."
"Good, that's settled then. You will be orange and I'll be purple,"
said Ollie.

20 January

Painting Morris

When Ollie and Morris told Mr Paintpot which colours they had chosen, he thought they had made a good decision. He got the orange paint first and picked up a large brush.

"Close your eyes," he said to Morris.

Morris shut his eyes tight. Then he felt a tickly wet brush stroking paint all over his body, which made him shiver. As Morris was only a small mouse, Mr Paintpot was soon finished.

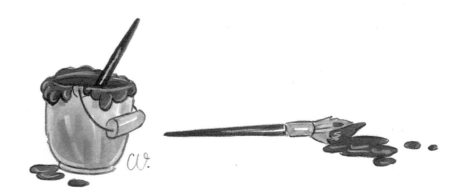

21 January

Painting Ollie

When Mr Paintpot finished painting Morris, Morris opened his eyes and looked in the mirror. He thought he looked quite wonderful! Then it was Ollie's turn. Ollie was about to be turned into a bright purple elephant!

Mr Paintpot fetched a huge bucket of paint. This was going to be a big job! After what seemed like hours and hours, Mr Paintpot took a large handkerchief from his pocket and wiped the sweat from his forehead. "At last! I've finished," he sighed with relief. "Purple really suits you Ollie!"

22 January

New colours

Ollie and Morris looked at each other. They were covered
in paint from head to toe. Ollie laughed at Morris.
He thought an orange mouse looked just a little bit silly!
Then Morris started to laugh too.
"Don't you like it?" asked Mr Paintpot, frowning.
"Yes, oh yes!" shouted Ollie and Morris. "We're really thrilled.
We want to go and show our friends."
"Mmmmm. I'm not quite sure about that,"
said Mr Paintpot.

23 January

Mr Paintpot's idea

Mr Paintpot looked hard at Ollie and Morris. Morris, the orange
mouse and Ollie, the purple elephant.
"You two are friends and your colours do look nice together,"
said Mr Paintpot.
"They are lovely colours, but something just isn't quite right."
Mr Paintpot thought long and hard. Ollie sighed.
"I've got it!" shouted Mr Paintpot.

24 January

Lots of stars

Mr Paintpot had an excellent idea. He was sure that something was missing, and now after thinking long and hard, he knew what it was! He picked up the purple brush and moved towards Morris.
"Hey, what are you doing?" asked Morris with surprise. "I chose orange not purple!"
"I'm going to paint purple stars on you, and then I'll paint orange stars on Ollie," replied Mr Paintpot.

25 January

Two good friends

Two good friends painted fresh and bright,
Ollie and Morris are glad,
Just as he said, Mr Paintbox was right,
Purple and orange don't look bad!

Two good friends stand up and cry
"What a huge change for us two,
They are wonderful colours, we shall certainly try
To keep them absolutely brand new."

Goodbye Mr Paintpot

Mr Paintpot was extremely proud when he had finished painting coloured stars on Ollie and Morris.
"Now you are finished," he said and smiled.
"Then it's time for us to go and celebrate!" cried Ollie.
"Thank you for painting us so beautifully."
"Yes, thank you Mr Paintpot. You have done a wonderful job. Goodbye," said Morris.
Ollie lifted Morris onto his head with his trunk. Off they both went, Morris singing happily and Ollie trumpeting loudly, on with their journey through Dreamland.

27 January

Dreamland colours

Ollie and Morris were so thrilled they forgot that they would only be those colours in Dreamland.
All the animals in Dreamland could choose new colours for themselves. Sebastian Squirrel had turned a beautiful shade of dark red. Bella Butterfly fluttered across to Morris.
"Hurrah!" she cried, "Now I'm not the only one who is a beautiful colour!"

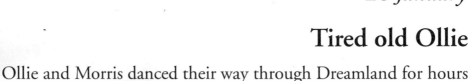

Tired old Ollie

Ollie and Morris danced their way through Dreamland for hours
and hours. Morris sung and called out to the other animals.
Ollie trumpeted enthusiastically. In no time at all, a long line of
singing and dancing animals was following Ollie and Morris – the
purple bear, the pink giraffe, a small yellow lion, a green hedgehog,
Sebastian Squirrel. The line was so long that it was hard to
see where it ended! Ollie's feet were starting to hurt.
"Phew!" he puffed, "Dreamland is enormous!"

29 January

Sore feet

"We're not going home yet, not for ages!" shouted Morris.
The little orange mouse was enjoying the view from the top of
Ollie's head. He didn't feel at all tired. But Ollie was the one
who had been dancing through Dreamland for hours. His feet
hurt. "I really must stop for a rest now Morris," he panted.
Gently he lowered Morris to the ground. Morris looked at
Ollie's big purple feet. "Oh, look!" he cried. "Poor Ollie,
you've got a blister. And another one here!"

30 January

The green hedgehog

Dancing through Dreamland for hours and hours
had been hard work for poor Ollie. His feet
throbbed and two big red blisters really hurt.
The green hedgehog felt sorry for Ollie.
"The best thing to do with blisters is to burst them," he said.
"Now, just sit still Ollie. I'm very good at bursting blisters!"
Ollie closed his eyes and felt a sharp prick. "Ow, ow. Don't!"
he shouted. He opened his eyes. And sat up straight with a fright.
What had happened? Ollie looked around. He saw his own room
and he was sitting in his own bed. He looked down at his legs, his
chubby grey legs. The blisters had disappeared. Ollie had been
dreaming. Is there such a place as Dreamland? Yes, there is, as
long as you shut your eyes tight and go to sleep. Go on, you'll see.

31 January

Dancing in Dreamland

Ollie was dancing in Dreamland
With Morris perched high on his head,
The others all found it so funny,
"Go Ollie, go!" they all said.

The animals were all painted brightly,
All beautiful colours you know,
Just close both your eyes very tightly
And straight off to Dreamland you'll go.

You suddenly wake up, it's morning,
"That was such a nice dream," you say.
You squeeze your eyes tight just to get the dream back,
But the dream has gone far, far away.

Norris Know-All

Norris was no ordinary elephant. Most elephants loved to have fun. They liked running, playing, rolling about in the mud and spraying water at each other. But not Norris. Norris much preferred to sit with his trunk in a book. He thought all this rushing about the place having fun was childish. When the others were playing hide-and-seek, Norris put on his glasses and read a book about the stars. When the others were playing tag, Norris got out a history book. That was why Norris knew a lot. And because he did, the others called him Norris Know-All. The other elephants liked having Norris Know-All around, because it meant they didn't have to read so many books themselves. If they had a question, they just asked Norris. And all the little elephants went to school every day, to Norris Know-All's school!

2 February

School

In a clearing in the forest was Norris Know-All's school.
Norris was a very clever elephant. Because he knew so much,
he gave lessons every morning to anyone who wanted to learn.
School began at nine o'clock sharp. Norris would cough once or
twice to silence everyone. When everyone was quiet, Norris started
the first lesson of the day. Sometimes he told stories about brave
elephant princes of long ago, or tales about other countries,
where the elephants looked quite different. Learning was fun
at Norris Know-All's school.

3 February

Norris Know-All, the teacher

Norris Know-All, the teacher
Is very wise and good,
He tells of things from long ago,
So listen as you should!

He knows the numbers one to ten,
And letters A to Z,
And when it comes to doing sums,
He does them in his head.

Three cheers for Norris Know-All,
His pupils love him so,
And when it's time for holidays
Nobody wants to go!

The search

Norris Know-All had lost his glasses, and without his glasses, Norris couldn't see anything at all. Where could he have put them? With a sigh, Norris crawled around, searching for his spectacles, but this wasn't very easy as he could hardly see anything. Without his glasses he couldn't even read a book, and Norris Know-All was at his happiest with his trunk in a good book.

He knew he had his glasses the night before because he was reading in bed. Perhaps his glasses had just slid off his trunk he thought. Norris ran to his bed, looked under the bed, looked under the pillow ... and yes! There were his glasses!

5 February

Advice from Norris

Norris Know-All was walking through the forest. As he walked along, he gave everyone advice. He showed the beavers how to build a dam. He told the woodpecker how to make a hole in a tree, and he warned the brown bear that he had to watch out for the bees when he stole their honey. Of course, the animals themselves didn't really need his advice. Sometimes they thought that Norris Know-All was a bit of an interfering busybody. But sometimes, luckily, his advice was useful.

"Don't dig your hole too close to the river," he warned Rebecca Rabbit. And when the river flooded after a heavy fall of rain, Rebecca Rabbit was very glad indeed that she had listened to his advice. Otherwise her burrow would have been completely flooded. Just imagine! What would have happened then to all her fluffy baby rabbits? So Rebecca Rabbit always said to her children, "You must listen to what Uncle Norris says, because without him we wouldn't have our nice warm, dry rabbit hole!"

A birthday present

It was nearly King Lion's birthday and all the animals were discussing what present they could give him.
"Does anybody have any ideas?" asked Rebecca Rabbit.
"Shall we give him a bunch of flowers?" suggested Morris Mouse.
"Or sing him a nice birthday song?" said Rupert Rhino.
"Or bake a cake?" asked Ollie.
They just couldn't agree. Then Norris Know-All had an idea.
"What about organising a big party with music, flowers, cakes and a play?" he suggested.
"That's a great idea. You are a clever elephant Norris!" cried all the animals.

7 February

Tubby

Tubby was Norris Know-All's cousin. Just like Norris and all the other elephants, he was round, fat and grey. But Tubby was much fatter. Tubby just loved chocolates. But ever since he had terrible toothache, poor Tubby wasn't allowed to eat any more chocolates.
Norris was a little bit suspicious when he saw Tubby one day. What was Tubby hiding behind his back?
"Now Tubby, I bet that's a bar of chocolate behind your back," said Norris.
"Don't be silly Norris. Of course it isn't. It's a book I borrowed from you last week. I'm bringing it back."
Norris turned as red as a ripe tomato.
He was ashamed of himself.

Football

Norris Know-All usually had his trunk in a book all day long.
When the other elephants went out to play football, Norris stayed
inside and read. But he knew all the rules of football by heart.
One day, there was an argument on the football pitch.
"It was a goal!"
"Wasn't!"
"Was!"
"Wasn't!"
Norris was fed up with all the shouting.
"What you need," he said, "is a referee. Someone who belongs to neither
side and who must be obeyed by everyone."
"What a good idea, Norris. Will you be our referee?"
So Norris Know-All joined in the football game after all. Whenever anyone
did anything wrong, Norris trumpeted loudly. All the animal players had to
do exactly as he said.
"Football is much more fun with you Norris," said Ollie after the match.

9 February

Orry the owl

Norris Know-All's best friend was Orry, the elderly owl. Orry was extremely old, but nobody knew quite how old. Orry was already around when Norris's grandfather was born. That's how old he was. Norris could talk to Orry for hours and hours about all sorts of things. There was, however, one small problem. Orry was rather deaf. And because he was old and stiff, he stayed high up in his tree. Norris couldn't even see where he was sitting. If he wanted to talk to Orry, Norris had to shout and shout until he was hoarse. But one day, Norris had an idea. He dragged some pieces of wood to Orry's tree and began to saw, hammer and chisel for quite some time. Ollie and Spike the hedgehog watched. "Whatever do you think Norris is making?" whispered Ollie. He was very curious.
Norris kept on working until the evening. He had made an elephant ladder, which he could use whenever he wanted to speak to Orry. He decided to try it out the next day.

10 February

The ladder

Orry the elderly owl was sitting on his favourite branch, dreaming.
Then he heard grunting and huffing and puffing. Sleepily, he opened one big,
yellow eye and saw his elephant friend, Norris.
"Who's this? Norris Know-All? Whatever are you doing here?"
"Hello Orry," panted Norris. "I've made a ladder so that I can climb up to see you
and then I can easily climb down again. Look, I'll show you."
Norris stepped down on to the next rung of the ladder, then the next and the next.
The ladder creaked. When Ollie stepped down on to the next rung, craaaccck!
The ladder broke. Poor old Norris crashed down to the ground
and landed on his fat elephant tummy. The whole forest shook.
Luckily Norris hadn't hurt himself. But he was sad that his plan had failed.

11 February

Lost

Norris could hear someone crying. He found a little rabbit sitting under the pine tree rubbing tears from her eyes.

"What's the matter?" asked Norris. He recognised little Rachel Rabbit straightaway. Rachel was one of Rebecca Rabbit's children.

"I'm lost," she sobbed. "We were playing hide-and-seek and now I can't remember the way home. I'll never find my mother again."

Norris, of course, knew where Rachel's house was. But as a teacher, he wanted Rachel to learn how to find the way home herself.

"Do you know what I do when I can't remember something?" asked Norris. "I sit down and have a good think. You should do that too. Can you remember what your rabbit hole looks like?" The little rabbit thought hard. "Our hole is under the roots of an oak tree. The tree trunk is so thick that at least a hundred rabbits could live under it." "There's only one tree with a trunk that thick in the whole forest," said Norris. "Old trees with thick trunks are often tall. If you look in the sky, you might be able to see it." Rachel looked at the tops of the trees. She could see the top of one tree way above all the others. "There!" she cried. "That must be the oak tree. Thank you very much Norris, you've been a great help."

She leaned towards Norris and gave him a big kiss.

12 February

Think and learn

You can look with your eyes
At everything around.
You can hear with your ears
Every little sound.
Your nose can tell you
If things smell nice or not.
Your mouth can tell
A nice taste, cold or hot.
But your head can think
And learn how to sing a song,
Or how to get to the top of the class,
Or tell what's right from wrong.

13 February

The headache

Norris Know-All had been thinking so hard that his
head ached. He tried walking around, sitting and lying
down, but nothing seemed to help. Bang, bang, bang
went his head. Poor Norris.
He tried to get some sleep. A good rest could cure a
headache. He snuggled down, took off his glasses
and closed his eyes. He was sure that he would soon
feel better.

Toadstools

Hoppy and Sniffy, the hares, were jumping happily through the long grass. Suddenly they saw some red toadstools in a field. "What are they?" asked Hoppy.

"I don't know," said Sniffy, "but they look tasty."

"Mmmm, those red caps with white spots look just like marzipan," said Hoppy, licking his lips.

Hoppy was just about to bite into one of the toadstools when Norris came along. "Don't!" shouted the elephant. "Those toadstools are very poisonous."

Hoppy and Sniffy jumped high into the air with fright. No more tasting toadstools for them they decided!

15 February

Why?

When Norris Know-All was still a very small elephant and had only just learned how to talk, he wanted to know about everything. He followed his mother around all day long and kept asking questions. "Why am I an elephant? Why am I small and you are big? Why does the sun shine?"

His mother answered his questions patiently until she had had quite enough. She decided to teach him a lesson. So she asked Norris a question. "Why are bananas bent?" Norris thought about this very carefully. And, do you know, he still doesn't know the answer.

Fishing

Norris Know-All had found his fishing rod. He was taking the day off. He didn't feel like thinking that day and it wasn't a school day.

Feeling happy, he walked down to the stream. He found a good place to sit and threw out his line. An hour later, he still hadn't caught a fish. Muttering darkly, he pulled the line in again.

"What's the matter?" asked Otto Otter, who just happened to be passing by.

"The fish just aren't biting," grumbled Norris.

"Did you put any bread on the hook?" laughed Otto. Oh, how stupid. Norris had completely forgotten about bait. No wonder the fish weren't biting. They weren't going to be interested in an empty hook.

Morris had forgotten that even when he had a day off, he still had to think!

Teasing

"Hey, silly four-eyes! Silly four-eyes!" the other elephants shouted at Norris Know-All. It wasn't his fault that he had bad eyesight. He wouldn't be without his glasses for the world. Without his glasses, Norris wouldn't be able to read any books. Norris thought the elephants who teased him were very silly. His glasses made him look very clever. Perhaps the other elephants were just jealous that they hadn't got a pair of brightly coloured glasses like his.

18 February

The letter

Rupert Rhino rushed in, out of breath. "Norris, I've just got a letter. But I don't understand any of it," he cried.
Norris Know-All looked up, surprised. "But Rupert, you can read, can't you?"
"Of course I can, but I still don't understand the letter!"
Rupert gave the letter to the clever elephant. Norris looked it and began to laugh. "I can see why you couldn't understand it Rupert. It's a letter from your cousin in France. He writes to tell you that he is coming to visit you soon."
"How nice," said Rupert, "but how will I talk to him? I can't speak French."
"I'll teach you some French words," promised Norris.

19 February

Winter

"Orry," Norris asked the elderly owl, "why am
I always a bit sad in the winter?"
"Everyone feels like that. It's because it's cold and dark.
Storms and rain don't make you feel very happy.
There are hardly any flowers or birds in the winter."
Norris Know-All nodded. Orry was right. It was no
fun without flowers and birds.
"But winter can be fun too," said Orry. "It's best if
there is snow and ice, because then you can go sledging
and skating. You can make snowmen too. But even if
there are just storms and rain, it can still be beautiful.
Look how the leaves whirl through the air in the
wind."
"Do you know what I like best about winter?" said
Norris. "When the sun shines through the bare
branches. It makes me feel warm inside."

20 February

The spider's web

Serena Spider was very cross. She had spun a beautiful
new web that morning and then the fierce wind had blown
it all to pieces. When Norris heard Serena complaining,
he felt sorry for her.
The little elephant thought long and hard.
He wondered how he could help Serena.
"What about weaving leaves into your web?"
he suggested. "That would keep the wind out."
"Yes, but it would keep the flies out too, and then what would
I eat?" replied Serena. Mmmm. Norris knew he needed
to think again.

21 February

Hibernation

Tubby, the fat little elephant, was looking for his friend Honeysweet
the bear. All summer long they had played and eaten
honey together. Suddenly Honeysweet had just disappeared.
Tubby had looked everywhere, but he hadn't seen Honeysweet for
ages. So he went to see his cousin, Norris Know-All. Perhaps
he would know what to do. He was always so clever.
"Of course I know where Honeysweet is," said Norris.
"Bears sleep in the winter. All summer long they eat and eat so their
tummies are full and round. Then, when it starts to get
colder, they return to their lairs and sleep until
the spring. It's called hibernating." Tubby was very
impressed that Norris knew all these things.

22 February

Fun on the ice

Norris woke up very early one morning. Brrr, wasn't it cold he thought. There was frost on his bedroom window. Norris even felt cold under his warm blanket.

He heard voices. The sound of laughter was coming from the direction of the lake. Quickly Norris got out of bed, put on a warm scarf and his red hat and ran outside. There was Rebecca Rabbit with her six baby rabbits. They were all dressed in hats and scarves and they all were carrying ice skates.

"Hey, Norris!" they all shouted at once. "Are you coming skating too?" Norris wanted to, but he couldn't skate. Each winter, he sat by the fire with a book. He had never even tried to skate. Silly Norris hadn't realised that learning to skate could be fun, even if it did mean falling over a lot!

44

23 February

Learning to skate

Norris Know-All followed Rebecca Rabbit and her children through the forest. The freezing air stung his trunk. The lake was completely frozen. The ice on the lake was so thick that all the animals in the forest had put on their skates. Norris stood at the side of the frozen lake. It did look fun, he thought, all the animals gliding and sliding about on the ice. After a while, his feet began to get cold. He stomped about a bit to get warm.
"Hey, Norris!" called Rachel Rabbit, "why don't you come on the ice too? We'll teach you how to skate!"
Ollie the little elephant lent Norris an old pair of skates.
Very carefully, Norris started to slide across the ice. He wasn't doing badly at all! Norris became a bit more confident until ... crash! He fell over with a huge thud. Craaacck! A large crack appeared right across the frozen lake. "Everyone off the ice quickly!" shouted Rebecca Rabbit.

45

The Professor

Most children want to be something exciting when they grow up. They might say they want to be a firefighter or an acrobat. But Norris Know-All knew what he wanted to be, and that was a professor.
That might not sound like much fun at all, but Norris had thought it through. He was going to solve very difficult problems. If he succeeded, everybody would be very grateful and his picture would be in all the newspapers. That would be so exciting Norris thought. And, actually, he thought that being a firefighter or an acrobat would be far too scary.

25 February

The flu

Orry, the elderly owl, was ill. His head and his throat hurt and he had a fever. What he really wanted to do was go to bed. But then what would happen to all the animals who came to ask for his advice, he thought.
Norris Know-All came to his assistance. The clever elephant sat at the bottom of the owl's tree and tried to help everyone as well as he could. Most of the animals were glad that Norris was helping out. But not Anastasia, the rather refined lady elephant. "Hah," thought Anastasia, "who does little Norris Know-All think he is? Does he really expect a person like me to ask advice from someone like him?"

26 February

A runny nose

It is very annoying I know,
But no matter how often you blow,
The stuff in your nose it just grows and it grows,
It simply refuses to go.

Sniffing won't help any more,
Nor will lying down flat on the floor.
You can stand on your head or hide under the bed
But it won't go away, I'm quite sure.

There is only one answer I know,
Invented so long, long ago,
Get your handkerchief out,
Wrap it well around your snout,
And just give it a jolly good blow.

27 February

A thief

In the autumn, the squirrels collected nuts and berries. They kept them in a secret hole. Then, when winter came, they always had something to eat. Norris Know-All went to see how the squirrels in the forest were getting on. But when he got near the squirrels' tree, the clever little elephant heard an angry voice. "Someone has stolen half my nuts and berries!"
Sebastian Squirrel was very cross. He had worked so very hard and now it had all been for nothing.
"Are you sure?" asked Norris. "Of course I'm sure. I'm not stupid. Where can I find a safe place for my nuts now?" said Sebastian.
Norris thought. "I have an idea. What about hiding the nuts under some very dirty berries? The thief won't like the look of those and will leave your real winter food alone."
"That's a good idea Norris. I'll do it straightaway," said Sebastian.

28 February

Pea soup

Norris Know-All had spent all day giving advice to the other animals. He had been so busy that he had forgotten to gather any wood. How was he going to light a fire? With a sigh, he began to collect some dead branches. The other animals noticed what Norris was doing and took pity on him. Rebecca Rabbit, Sebastian Squirrel and Ollie the little elephant all brought him a stick or a branch. Even Orry the owl stretched his stiff, elderly legs and brought Norris a twig.

"It's because you have always been such a good help to us," they said. Norris was touched.

"Do you know what?" he said. "I'm going to make a big pan of pea soup. And you must all come and have supper with me."

All the animals went home to collect something nice to eat with the pea soup. Rebecca Rabbit got some carrots, Sebastian Squirrel some nuts, and Ollie brought some bread. When they returned, they could smell the pea soup. It smelled delicious. Norris wasn't just clever, they thought, he was a good cook too!

29 February

Suppertime

Suppertime, suppertime for one and all,
Animals large and animals small,
Gather around a great big pot,
Some get a little, some get a lot!

Eating is best if it's done with others,
Fathers, mothers, sisters, brothers,
Pea soup, carrots and sausage in a pan,
Eat up just as much as you can.

Eat until you can eat no more,
Stop before your tummy gets sore.
Too many sweet things are bad for you,
"Pea soup is better" is very true.

49

1 March

The circus

The circus was coming to town, so everyone was excited. A long line of circus wagons made its way to Farmer Daley's field. There were brightly coloured caravans where the circus people lived, wagons filled with balls and hoops, and cages full of animals. In one of the cages sat Leonard Lion. He yawned to show off his strong white teeth. People thought that this was very exciting. Then there was a van full of lovely things to eat – lollipops, liquorice, candyfloss and popcorn.
In the last three wagons was a family of elephants – John-John, his wife Laura, their son, Elliot, and their daughter, Lizzie. Lizzie wriggled with pleasure, making the wagon rock from side to side. She had to watch out. The wagon could have easily toppled over!

2 March

Wibble wobble wagon

Wibble wobble wagon,
I wobble in my wagon.
I bounce from wall to wall,
Wibble wobble wagon,
I wobble in my wagon,
I'm sure I'm going to fall!

Slow down, wobbly wagon,
Slower, wobbly wagon.
I think I'm going to shout,
"Slow down, wobbly wagon,
Slower, wobbly wagon,
LET ME OUT!"

3 March

Putting up the tent

Lizzie the circus elephant had arrived in Bumblebury with
her father, mother and brother. Before the circus could begin,
they had to put up the big top. First of all, the circus people fixed
the tent poles in place with thick ropes. Then they put the
canvas cover on the top. It was red and yellow, which looked
bright and cheerful. Once the canvas was on, the big top was
ready, except for the benches, which had to be put inside.
The people would be sitting on them the next night
when the show would begin. But what was
Lizzie doing? Lizzie was hanging up brightly
coloured flags with her trunk!

4 March

Spring is coming

Lizzie was strolling through the fields with her
brother Elliot. "Phew," puffed Elliot, "what a lot
of work! I'm really tired now." Lizzie giggled.
"You, tired? How can you be? You hardly did
anything!"
"Oh yes I did!" cried Elliot angrily.
He was so cross that he didn't look where he was going.
"Look out!" cried Lizzie. "You almost trod on some
crocuses. Look how pretty they are. Yellow and
purple crocuses."
The two little elephants thought they were delightful.
They had completely forgotten their argument.
"Spring is coming, isn't it, Lizzie?" said Elliot.

Do not pick the crocuses

Elliot stuck out his trunk to pick the crocuses. "Don't!" cried a little voice. It was Colin the Coaltit. Elliot quickly pulled back his trunk. "You're not allowed to pick crocuses. They will die very quickly, even if you put them in water."
"What a shame," sighed Elliot. "I wanted to take some back for Mother."
"I know," said Lizzie, "let's go and get her, then she can see the crocuses too!"

6 March

Crocus song

Little sleeping crocus
Under the warm dark ground,
Dreaming in your little bulb,
Sleeping, oh so sound.

Little crocus, wake up!
Under the warm dark ground,
Creep out of your little bulb
And have a look around.

53

Bathtime

It was that day again. Laura, Lizzie and Elliot's mother, called out to her children, "Bathtime, Lizzie! Bathtime, Elliot!" There was William, the elephant-keeper. He was carrying mops, scrubbing brushes and big buckets full of soapy water. He was going to scrub the elephant family clean. Lizzie and Elliot ran up. "Slow down you two, where's the fire?" laughed William. He soaked the mops and brushes in the soap suds and started work. It took a whole hour to get Elliot clean. Scrubbing elephants was hard work!

Getting dressed

William had scrubbed all the circus elephants until they were gleaming! "Oh, aren't we lovely and clean!" squealed Lizzie. Then it was the elephants' favourite bit … they had to get dressed. William gave them their circus clothes, which he had carefully washed and ironed. They were beautiful. Four colourful blankets edged with golden tassels to put on the elephants' backs and four beautiful hats with feathers. William helped to dress the elephants, first Elliot, then Lizzie, followed by Laura, and lastly John-John. They looked wonderful!

9 March

Smile please!

A large bustling crowd had arrived to watch the circus. All the people from the local town had come. When they saw the elephant family, they cried, "Look at the elephants! Aren't they beautiful?" One man got out his camera. "I must take a photograph of them," he said. The elephants John-John, Laura, Lizzie and Elliot stood together. "Curl trunks!" ordered John-John. The camera flashed. "When the photograph is printed, I'll give you a copy," promised the man.

10 March

Buying tickets

There was a long queue at the entrance to the tent, where people were waiting to buy a ticket to get in to the circus. Helena was selling tickets. So many tickets! She felt really hot and bothered. Lizzie noticed that Helena was feeling faint and so she ran over to her to see if she could help. All the people moved aside. "Give me the book of tickets Helena and I'll tear them off for you," she said. They could work much faster together, and the people rather liked taking their tickets from Lizzie's trunk!

11 March

Find Lizzie

"Elliot, go and get Lizzie! We're on in a minute,"
said John-John, their father.
The big top was full of people. The ringmaster
welcomed the audience and announced the acts.
First were the dancers. They were wearing pretty,
glittering dresses and feathers in their hair. Then the
elephants would go on. Elliot rushed out into the field.
Where had Lizzie got to? He asked Leonard Lion.
"Lizzie?" yawned Leonard. "Lizzie went that way,
I think."
Elliot couldn't understand it. He looked everywhere,
but couldn't find his sister anywhere. Was Lizzie
hiding?

12 March

Little sister, where are you?

Little sister, where are you?
In the grass so tall,
I'll come and hide beside you too,
So give a little call.

Little sister, where are you?
I've called and called all day,
But still I don't know where you are
And I do so want to play!

56

Stage fright

Lizzie was sitting quietly behind a big tree. She had lost her nerve. She was so afraid of making a mistake. She had to spin a big ball decorated with stars on the tip of her trunk, and Lizzie was quite sure that she couldn't do it. She did it that afternoon, but she was sure she couldn't do it now!
Lizzie had stage fright.
What was that noise?
"Lizzie, where are you? We're on in a minute, Lizzie!" It sounded like Elliot.
Lizzie wasn't sure what to do.
"Oh, come on, Lizzie. You're not going to leave me to go on on my own, are you?"
Let Elliot down? No, Lizzie would never do that.
"I'm coming," she shouted.

14 March

All the elephants in the ring

In the middle of the big top there was a circle of sand covering the floor. This was the circus ring, where the circus animals and people performed. The ringmaster stood in the middle and cried out, "Ladies and Gentlemen! Children! A nice round of applause please for the Elephant Family!"
The music rang out. And there they were. Leading the way was John-John, followed by Laura, then Lizzie, and, at the back, Elliot. The biggest in front and the smallest at the back. They were holding on to each other, forming a train of elephants. Laura was holding John-John's tail with her trunk, Lizzie was holding Laura's tail, and Elliot Lizzie's!

57

Lizzie's act

The drums rolled. With knees trembling, Lizzie walked to the middle of the circus ring. "Good luck Lizzie!" whispered Elliot. "You can do it!"
There was William, the elephant-keeper. He was wearing a splendid costume, white trousers and a red jacket with gold buttons and gold braid. He was holding a big blue ball decorated with gold stars. He threw the ball high into the air. "Catch Lizzie!" cried William. The drums rolled again ... and, yes, Lizzie caught the ball on the tip of her trunk. But she didn't stop there. She was spinning the ball too! The audience were thrilled and clapped and cheered.

16 March

Jane

Jane had come to the circus with her father. They were sitting right at the front. They could see everything. First of all came the beautiful dancers, and then the elephants. Jane liked the elephants best, especially Lizzie.
"Look!" she cried with delight. "Isn't that little elephant clever? She can spin a ball on her trunk so easily!"
Jane's father thought Lizzie was amazing too.
"Daddy, may I go and look at the elephants after the show?" asked Jane.
"Of course you may," replied her father. "I'd like to see them too."

17 March

Applause

Everyone applauded the elephant,
With her trunk she could do
a good trick,
Such as spinning a ball without
letting it fall,
Or beating a drum with a stick.

Everyone applauded the elephant,
She could use her trunk like a hand.
She could trumpet "Tara"
and "Ta-ran-ta-ran-ta"
And march at the front of the band.

18 March

Tired but happy

After the performance, the elephants marched off in a line back to their wagons. William ran along behind them. "Well done!" he laughed. "Did you hear how the audience clapped? You really did your best. You're the cleverest elephants I know."

John-John's eyes sparkled with pleasure, Laura's trunk twitched with pride, and Lizzie and Elliot jumped about with delight.

"Phew, I really am tired," sighed Lizzie as she climbed into her wagon.

"A nice bowl of food and a bucket of water for each of you," said William, "then early to bed for a good sleep."

19 March

Visitors

Jane's father had promised that she could
visit the circus elephants.
"I thought your act was wonderful" Jane said.
"I wanted to come and tell you myself.
Thank you so much!" She took hold
of Lizzie's trunk and shook it.
From behind her back she produced
a beautiful bunch of flowers.
"Thank you," trumpeted the elephants
together. "We are so pleased that
you enjoyed the show. We put
on our best performance."

20 March

Fresh flowers

William put the
beautiful flowers in a bright blue
bucket filled with water.
Elephants have a much
better sense of smell than
we have, because of
their long trunks.
Elliot smelled the
delicate scent of the
tulips and freesias and
thought of jungles filled
with tropical plants and
ripe fruit. Hey, what
was Elliot up to?
He wasn't meant to
eat the flowers!

The first day of Spring

Lizzie got up very early that morning. She didn't know why, but she felt like going outside. Father, Mother and Elliot were still asleep.

Lizzie crept out quietly. She stood quite still for a moment and smelled the cool, fresh morning air. Lizzie flapped her ears. She did that whenever she felt happy. There must have been a hundred birds in the big tree at the edge of the stream. Tweet tweet! Cheep cheep!

"Why are you making so much noise?" asked Lizzie.

"Silly little elephant," said Belinda Blackbird. "Don't you know? Today is the first day of Spring. All the birds are excited."

Lizzie then understood why she wanted to go outside. She sensed the excitement in the air and it made her feel happy. She raced round the field with delight. Who was racing over towards her? It was Elliot! He was flapping his ears too!

22 March

Spring-cleaning

"It's such lovely weather," said Laura, their mother. "I shall clean everything today."
Helped by William, Laura got to work. First, they carried everything outside – the buckets, the bowls for food, and the bales of straw. William hung the their circus clothes on the line. Then he filled up a big bowl with soapy water. He took a brush, dipped it into the soap suds and began to scrub the floor. Laura cleaned the floor differently, by sticking her trunk into the water, sucking up a trunkful and then ... whoosh! She sprayed all the walls.

23 March

John-John

John-John was a very large circus elephant with beautiful big tusks. He was the star of the circus. When he stood on his back legs and curled up his trunk, the audience cheered and shouted with admiration. Even Leonard Lion couldn't beat that! That day John-John was being kicked out of his house. Laura wanted to spring-clean and she didn't want any spectators. John-John wandered around the wagons. He was bored and felt sorry for himself. John-John didn't have much time for spring-cleaning!

24 March

Duckweed

Elliot was walking in the fields. The spring sun was shining and the birds were singing at the top of their voices. In the big tree by the stream, Belinda and Billy Blackbird were busy building a nest.
"Your nest is bound to be the best nest that was ever built!" said Elliot encouragingly.
"Tweet tweet!" said Belinda. "I can't reach properly. Move out of the way!"
"Do you need any help?" asked Elliot. He watched what Belinda was doing. The stream was full of duckweed. So full, in fact, that you could hardly see the water. Elliot had been watching Belinda so closely that he didn't see it. He stepped out to help her and fell with a huge splash into the water.
"Tweet tweet tweet!" laughed Belinda. "I've never seen anything so funny. A green elephant!"

25 March

A dirty elephant

Mother elephant and William had finished their spring-cleaning. They were pleased with their work. Everything sparkled in the spring sunshine. Sweet, fresh straw had been laid in every wagon, the food bowls had all been scrubbed, and the clothes were fresh and clean. Then Laura heard Elliot's voice.
"Mummy, mummy, come and look!"
The door swung open and in stepped Elliot. Laura screamed with fright. There was little Elliot covered in green slime and dripping with water from the stream. "Oh, you naughty little elephant! I'll have to start all over again now," sighed Laura.

26 March

A new trick

Lizzie could do a very clever trick. She had been practising it with William. Audiences always liked this trick. William threw their ball high into the air and Lizzie caught it and spun it on her trunk. Claude Clown came along one day while she was practising.

"Ah ha, Lizzie. Are you practising your trick again?"

"Yes," said Lizzie, "because I'm always afraid I'll make a mistake."

"I don't believe a word of it," laughed Claude. "You could do that trick in your sleep. You'll never make a mistake. You should really think up a new trick."

"A new trick?" thought Lizzie, frowning. "What sort of trick?" she asked.

"Do you know what? I'll help you think of one," said Claude Clown.

You're joking!

Claude Clown decided to help Lizzie invent a new trick.
"It must be something really new," he said excitedly. "Like jumping through
a hoop at the same time as spinning a ball on your trunk, or jumping through a
burning hoop, or juggling with fresh cream cakes ... "
Lizzie thought that all these ideas sounded very difficult.
Jumping through a burning hoop? Never!
"I know!" she shouted out suddenly. "I'll pick you up with my trunk, swing you
round in the air three times and drop you on you nose on to a fresh cream cake!"
Claude Clown went very quiet. Then he saw the twinkle in Lizzie's eye.
"You're joking!" he giggled. Although he didn't really mind about being
dropped on to a fresh cream cake!

28 March

A funny trick

"What do you
think about doing a
trick together?" asked Claude.
"That could be fun," answered Lizzie,
" but if you join in, Claude, it will have to
be a funny trick. You are a clown, after all,
and clowns are supposed to make people laugh."
"A funny trick. That's a very good idea Lizzie. So, I'll do
the funny bit, and you can do the difficult bit."
Claude Clown thought that this was a good plan.
"Yes, you could keep trying to climb on my back and
I keep could keep walking away, and then ..."
Lizzie was picturing the plan in her head.
"Or you could do your spinning the ball trick and
I could shoot it off with my water pistol," cried Claude.
"If we go and practise now, we could put it
in tomorrow's show," said Lizzie.
Lizzie and Claude were busy all afternoon.
They were having a
marvellous time!

67

29 March

No peeping

Whatever could Lizzie have been doing all this time? Elliot wanted to know where she could be. He crept up to the tent and lifted up a corner of the canvas with his trunk. He could see Claude standing at the top of a ladder. He was holding a bucket of water. He was wobbling about like mad. Suddenly Claude noticed Elliot. "Hey Elliot, no peeping!" he shouted. Oh no, the ladder started to shudder. Over toppled Claude and the bucket of water landed right on top of his head! Poor Claude. Elliot thought he better not stay around as Claude probably wouldn't be very happy. Playing outside would be safer!

30 March

A brilliant trick!

At last Claude's and Lizzie's new trick was ready. A paddling pool and a diving board were in the middle of the circus ring. The drums began to roll and Lizzie and Claude made their entrance. Claude was wearing his swimming costume. Was he going to dive into the water? It certainly looked like he was. He climbed up to the diving board. Lizzie was watching from the side.
"Look out! I'm going to dive!" shouted Claude to Lizzie. He bounced up and down on the diving board and jumped high into the air ... falling, falling and then landing slap bang on Lizzie's back! The audience cheered and clapped. Claude climbed up to the diving board again, jumped high into the air again, but, that time, Lizzie caught him with her trunk. On the third attempt Claude actually landed in the water and, as he spluttered to the surface, Lizzie sprayed him with a trunkful of water.
Everybody roared with laughter and cheered again!

31 March

Long live the circus!

The circus is over, we all shout "Goodbye!"
But I trumpet loudest of all.
We'll see you next year, so be sure you are here,
Yes be sure you are here when we call.

So I'll blow you a very big trumpeting kiss,
And next year we'll come back once more.
So long live the circus and come back quite soon,
We'll be waiting for you at the door.

1 April

Ali

Ali the elephant lived in a distant land called Arabia, where it was always lovely and warm and dry. The sun shone all day long there, every day of the year.
Ali was no ordinary elephant. He lived in the sultan's palace. The sultan was the ruler of the country and he was very rich. Together with his father and mother, aunts and uncles, Ali lived in the splendid stables with the horses.
The other extraordinary thing about Ali was that he was born with shimmering pink skin. When the sun shone, he glistened so beautifully that it seemed as if his skin was made of mother-of-pearl.

2 April

Morning exercises

The first rays of sun streamed through the windows, warming Ali's trunk. The little elephant woke with a start. He shook off the straw and looked at the other elephants. They were still asleep. Ali tip-toed outside. His legs still felt a little bit stiff after his long sleep, so Ali decided to do some exercises.
One, two, one, two. He bent his knees. He waved his trunk from left to right.
Ali's body began to stir. He was starting to feel so much better.

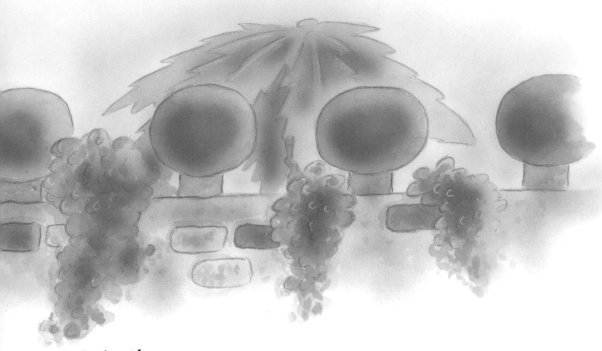

3 April

The sultan's palace

Ali's breakfast hadn't arrived. He wondered whether the elephant-keepers had overslept. They should have definitely brought it by this time. He began to pace back and forth impatiently. "Should I go and find out where they are?" he thought. He started to look around. Not a keeper in sight. The only thing he could see was the sultan's palace. "Isn't the palace beautiful!" sighed Ali. "I'd love to be the sultan. Then I could live in that lovely tower with the golden roof."

4 April

Nosy parker

Ali really wanted to have a look inside the sultan's palace. But elephants belonged in the stables, not in the palace, and, although the stables were very nice, Ali couldn't help being curious.
"I am a special elephant, after all," he reasoned. "I have shimmering pink skin, so I should get special treatment." Unfortunately, the palace guards didn't agree.
"About turn, little elephant. Back to the stables you go. You don't belong in a palace."

5 April

Keep out!

You are a small pink elephant
And special, that's quite true,
But you may not have your own way
For that just would not do.
If you went to the palace
You'd get stuck in the door,
And vases, china, precious things
Would crash down to the floor.
Yes you are a very special case,
Of that there is no doubt,
But though you may not like it,
Stay at home. Keep out! Keep out!

6 April

In disguise

Ali was as stubborn as a mule. Once he had an idea in his head, that was it. Ali had decided to look inside the sultan's palace. He had already thought of a plan. Taking a long piece of cloth, he wound it around his head to make a turban. Then he took another piece of material and draped it over his body. "I'll pretend to be a stranger who has come from another country to visit the sultan," he muttered. He would have to see if the palace guards would fall for his disguise.

7 April

Princess Fatima

The sultan had a daughter, Princess Fatima. Fatima was not just very beautiful, she was very sweet-natured. She was kind to everyone, and she loved animals. Fatima often visited the stables, although they weren't really a suitable place for a princess. She walked daintily through the straw in her silver slippers. She carried a basket of delicious figs. Ali was waiting for her.
"Here you are, dear little elephant," she said, and she gave Ali some figs. Ali was delighted and gave the princess a big kiss with his trunk.

8 April

A strange princess

Princess Fatima went to the palace stables almost every day. She always took something with her – figs for the elephants or sugar-lumps for the horses. She really wanted to look after all the animals herself, but it wasn't thought suitable for a real princess to do that. "Oh dear," she sighed from time to time, "I'd much rather live here than in that rich palace." Ali couldn't believe his ears. "Rather live here in the stables than in the beautiful palace? What a strange princess!" he thought.

9 April

The fountain

It was a beautiful morning and Fatima, the sultan's daughter, had come to see the animals again. "Will you come with me?" she asked Ali the little pink elephant. Ali was thrilled. He wanted to ask her where they were going and what they were about to do, but elephants can't talk, and if he had trumpeted, the princess wouldn't have understood him. So Ali followed the princess. Princess Fatima strolled through the palace gardens, where beautiful flowers were in full bloom. Then Ali saw a fountain among the palms and banana trees. Ali loved water. He forgot that he was out for a walk with the princess and ran to the fountain, sucked up a trunkful of water and sprayed it all over himself. Oh dear, he had forgotten all about the princess. Fatima was soaking wet too! Luckily she saw the funny side of it and laughed.

75

10 April

A parade

Once a week the sultan visited the city. It was always a great event, because the sultan didn't go on foot. That would not be distinguished enough for a sultan. The sultan rode on an elephant. There wasn't just one elephant, but a whole train of elephants. Even Ali the little elephant was allowed to go, and he was given a gold embroidered blanket to wear on his back. He looked magnificent.
The elephants walked slowly through the narrow streets of the city. Ali was amazed at how much there was to see.

11 April

The bazaar

In the middle of the city there was a bazaar. Brightly coloured stalls lined the street, selling food, jewellery, clothes and carpets.
Ali was proud to be walking in the sultan's parade. He was the smallest elephant, so he took his place at the back.
On one of the stalls there were dates and figs. Ali adored figs.
As he approached the stall, he could smell the figs and his mouth started to water. He didn't know whether to take one or not.
Ali didn't realise that he had to pay for them as he wasn't used to carrying money at the palace.

12 April

Favourite food

If you could choose your favourite food,
What would you choose and why?
Would it be chips, ice-cream or cheese?
Would it be apple pie?

Ali didn't need to think,
No really, not at all,
Because the little elephant
Liked figs the best of all.

Stop thief!

The figs looked so tempting, it was hard to resist them. Suddenly he heard a shout. "Stop thief!" He saw someone running away and lots of other people were chasing him. Then he heard someone else say, "What is the world coming to? Somebody has stolen something from one of the stalls again. These thieves don't even think of paying." Ali's ears pricked up. Paying? He hadn't thought of that. With a sigh, he took a last lingering look at the figs and turned away.

14 April

The fig-seller

The fig-seller laughed. He realised that Ali the little elephant loved figs. He noticed how Ali swallowed, sighed deeply and turned without touching the figs.
"You are a very good little elephant," he said. "You haven't got any money, so you leave the figs alone."
Ali looked at the man with surprise. Surely it was obvious. Ali certainly wasn't a thief!
"Because you've been so good, I'm going to give you a fig. Absolutely free," laughed the fig-seller. As Ali bit into the ripe, juicy fig, he thought how kind and generous the fig-seller was.

15 April

The new arrival

Ali was having an afternoon snooze. It was quiet in the palace stables.
The straw was nice and soft, and the thick walls kept the stable cool.
Ali was gently snoring.
Suddenly, he woke up. What was all that noise?
What were the keepers doing in the stables at this time
of day? He got up to have a look. He could see that
the keepers were bringing a new animal into
the stables. It had a curved neck and two
big humps on its back.

16 April

Caroline Camel

Ali was surprised that a new animal was going
to share the stables with him.
"I'm Ali," he said politely. "Why have you got
humps on your back?"
The animal looked at Ali. It had huge, gentle,
brown eyes with long lashes.
"I am Caroline Camel. Camels always have
humps on their backs. Some have one
hump and some have two. We store food
in them. Sometimes we have to go on long
journeys into the desert, where there is no
food. Then we can use the food stored in
our humps."
"Oh I see," said Ali, "so it's a little bit like
carrying a lunchbox!"

17 April

To the river

The keepers at the sultan's palace looked after the animals very well. They knew that the elephants loved water. So, once a week, they took the animals to the river. Ali always looked forward to the outing.

"Tarantara tarantara," he trumpeted happily. "Bathtime again today. Hurrah!"

Usually, Ali trundled along behind the other elephants, but on the way to the river he got quite impatient. "Come on you lot, get a move on!" he shouted to the others.

18 April

Mud

The sultan's elephants were bathing lazily in the river. Their keepers had given them all a good wash. Then the elephants had sprayed each other. "I don't feel like lazing about," said Ali, his pink skin gleaming. He got up and walked to the riverbank. Suddenly, his legs began to sink into the mud. The mud felt soft and warm. Ali was looking forward to a mud bath. In no time at all, his skin was no longer a beautiful shiny pink, but dark and splattered with mud. "Oh Ali!" groaned the keepers, "now we'll have to start all over again!"

A caravan

Ali saw a large group of camels on the riverbank. Some were drinking, and others were squatting on the ground with their long legs folded underneath their bodies, snoozing in the hot sun. Ali was curious. He walked over to see the camels.
"Hello, I'm Ali and I live in the sultan's palace," he said.
"Hello Ali," replied one of the camels. "My name is Caspar and I live everywhere and nowhere. Mustapha, my master, and I travel through the desert carrying goods that Mustapha can sell in the towns." "Just the two of you?" asked Ali.
"No," answered Caspar, "a lot of camels travel together. It's called a caravan."

20 April

The lamp

Ali watched Caspar as he and the other camels left for their journey to the next town. Parcels and bundles hung from the camels' backs. Ali now knew that these parcels were filled with things that could be sold at the bazaars. He wondered what Caspar's master sold. Then Ali noticed something sparkling in the sand. He blew away the sand with his trunk. It was a shiny oil lamp. So Caspar's master sold lamps. "I'll look after the lamp," Ali decided.

Mischief

Little Ali, good as gold,
Mostly did as he was told.
But from time to time he could be
Mischievous enough for three!

Big broad smile upon his face,
To the river he would race,
"Naughty boy!" his mother would scold,
"Where is Ali, good as gold?"

22 April

Monkey business

Ali liked monkeys. They chattered and
climbed trees. They always seemed to be
having fun. Ali stood under the monkey
trec and said, "Hello, funny monkeys,
how are you?"
"Funny monkeys?" said a voice from the tree.
"We'll show you how funny we are. Catch this!"
Suddenly, the tree was raining coconuts.
Bonk! A coconut fell on Ali's head. He was
very angry. Wrapping his trunk round one of
the coconuts, he threw it towards the monkeys.
Unfortunately his aim wasn't very good.
He heard the sound of breaking glass. He had
broken somebody's window!

The elephant market

Ali was in big trouble. He had broken one of the palace windows. His mother was extremely cross! "But I didn't do it on purpose," cried Ali, with tears in his eyes. "I am ashamed of you Ali," grumbled his mother. "Do you know what happens to naughty little elephants?"
"No," whispered Ali. "Naughty elephants get sold at the Elephant Market," explained his mother. "It's a horrible place. They put chains on you and you have to stand in the hot sun until someone buys you. And you can't choose your new master, you know. A master chooses you, and he might be mean and nasty."
This warning frightened little Ali. He promised his mother that he would be good.

24 April

An important visitor

Music rung out from the sultan's palace. Trumpet, drums, cymbals and horns. Music everywhere.
Ali rushed outside to see what was happening. The sultan was welcoming a visitor, an uncle from a distant land. The uncle was also a sultan, and also very rich, so he had brought lots of expensive presents with him to show just how rich he was.
Ali couldn't believe his eyes. So many presents! Princess Fatima opened a box containing a beautiful gold necklace.
"I wonder if I'll get a present too?" thought Ali.

25 April

The present

Ali jumped up and down impatiently. He had heard that the sultan's visitor had brought everyone a present.
"I really hope he hasn't forgotten me," muttered Ali.
A few minutes later, the keepers came into the stables, their arms full of beautiful blankets. They put a new blanket on the back of each elephant. Ali got one too.
"Oh, I wish I had a mirror," he said proudly, "then I could see how beautiful I look!"

A flying carpet

Proud as a peacock, Ali paraded around, showing off
his new blanket. He wanted everyone to see how
beautiful he looked.
"Blanket," said Ali, "you may be beautiful,
but you make my back itch."
To Ali's astonishment, the blanket answered him.
"I do that on purpose," it said.
"You can talk?" Ali was astonished.
"Yes, I am a magic blanket," said the voice.
"Actually, I am a flying carpet."
"Really? Then show me how you can fly," said Ali.
"No, I don't feel like it at the moment," replied the
carpet. "I much prefer lying on your back.
It's much less tiring."

27 April

The snooty horse

Ali had decided to go exploring. He had never seen the animals who lived in the other part of the stables. He trotted merrily through the different stalls and greeted everyone with a wave of his trunk and a jolly cry. "Good morning!" he shouted out happily.
"And Good morning to you too!" answered all the animals.
At the last stall, Ali got no reply. Ali peeped over the edge of the door and saw a beautiful horse.
"Why didn't you say 'Good morning' like all the others?" Ali asked the horse. "Because I'm not like all the others," replied the horse snootily. "I'm a pure thoroughbred."
"Well, I'm a thoroughbred too!" Ali blurted out.

28 April

A thoroughbred elephant

"Mother, is a thoroughbred really so special?" asked Ali.
"Yes, thoroughbreds are very expensive horses," explained his mother. "They are bred with the greatest of care and they can run very fast."
"But I can run fast too," said Ali. "Does that mean I'm a thoroughbred as well?"
"Yes," laughed his mother, "you're a thoroughbred elephant!"

29 April

A competition

"Shall we see who can run the fastest?" said Ali to Pasha, the thoroughbred horse. "The winner gets a banana."
Pasha thought that this was hilarious. An elephant challenging a racehorse! "Ready, steady, go!" shouted Ali. They got off to a flying start, but Ali quickly dropped behind. He began to huff and puff. Pasha glanced across to Ali, realising that the poor little elephant was getting very tired. Feeling a bit sorry for Ali, he slowed down. Ali huffed and puffed and managed to catch up with the sleek horse. Crossing the finish line together, Ali was overjoyed.
"You deserve the banana," said Pasha. "I honestly didn't realise you could run so fast. And, anyway, horses don't like bananas."

30 April

A champion

Ali is a champion,
He's very good, a winner,
He won't stop, not for anyone,
Well, perhaps once, just for dinner!

He wants to race with everyone,
No matter how short or tall,
"I am the fastest elephant,
The fastest one of all!"

87

1 May

Trumpeter

Trumpeter the mischievous elephant was in a very good mood. He strolled through the park. The sun shone and Trumpeter felt marvellous. The nice weather cheered everyone up. The children in the playground were having a whale of a time, and it seemed as if there were twice as many birds singing as usual. Sparrows, blackbirds and starlings flew around in the warm spring air. "You're all very busy!" called out Trumpeter to the birds. "Why don't you just relax and enjoy the sunshine?"

"Oh, we are enjoying the sunshine," replied the birds. "It is beautiful weather for building nests. You do remember, don't you, that all the birds lay their eggs in May?"

2 May

Lay their eggs

In May, in May,
The birds do lay.
The blackbird, robin and the jay
Lay their eggs from day to day.

In May, in May,
The birds do lay.
The bluetit, magpie and the thrush
Lay their eggs in tree or bush.

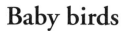

Baby birds

All the birds were busy building their nests. The hen birds would soon lay their eggs, and then it wouldn't be long before Trumpeter would hear the twitter of baby birds in every nest. Trumpeter loved baby birds. They were so tiny and soft. Baby birds needed lots of care and attention and lots of food, so they kept their parents very busy indeed.

4 May

Sad music

Trumpeter heard music playing in the distance. He could just hear the sound of trumpets and drums. He tramped off to find out what was happening. He wondered where the music was coming from. As he marched along, he swung his trunk from side to side in time with the music. But the nearer he got to the music, the lower his trunk drooped. It wasn't cheerful music; it was very gloomy music. Not the right sort of music for such a nice day! Trumpeter listened for a minute and decided to leave the gloomy music behind.

5 May

Happy music

The next day Trumpeter could hear music again, but this time the band was playing cheerful tunes and all the musicians were wearing bright red suits with gold buttons.

"Why weren't you playing like this yesterday?" Trumpeter asked. "Because we were playing for someone who was sad," answered the conductor. "Today we're playing happy music because it's a holiday. Music can tell you what sort of a day it is and what sort of mood someone is in."

6 May

Tuba

Trumpeter listened to the band. His favourite instrument was the tuba. The tuba player had to blow his cheeks out to get the low notes. A big, fat bumblebee buzzed around the tuba player's head and swooped down and stung his cheek. "Ow!" screamed the tuba player. His cheek throbbed so much that it was impossible for him to blow the tuba. The other musicians didn't know what to do. The music didn't sound half so good without the tuba. Trumpeter raised his trunk and asked, "Can I help?" So Trumpeter joined the band. Pom, pom, pom, pom, pom, pom, padapom, he played. Trumpeter was getting more confident with every note.

7 May

A party

"I'm having a party. Will you come?"
Trumpeter asked his friends. They all were
delighted to accept his invitation.
"What sort of a party is it?" wondered
Max Mouse.
"I bet it's a birthday party," said Peter Peacock.
"If it is his birthday, then we'll have to take a
present." said Henry Hare. "I wonder what
Trumpeter would like?"

8 May

A problem

Max Mouse, Peter Peacock and Henry Hare didn't
know what to give Trumpeter for his birthday.
They were fed up. They couldn't go to his
birthday party without taking a
birthday present.
"I can't think of anything," sighed Peter at last.
"I give up." Max had a suggestion. "Let's ask
Porker Pig. He's Trumpeter's best friend.
He's bound to be able to help."

9 May

Just for fun

Max Mouse, Peter Peacock and Henry Hare set off to visit Porker
Pig. Porker lived on a farm with a huge mud patch at the back.
"Porker, Porker!" shouted Max, Peter and Henry.
"Can you help us?"
Porker appeared. "What's the matter?" he asked.
"Can you think of a present for Trumpeter? We've all been invited
to his party, but we don't know what to give him."
"You can ask him yourself. He just happens to be here at the
moment. He came to visit me."
When Trumpeter heard why his friends had come to see Porker,
he laughed. "But it's not my birthday. It's just a party. For fun.
I don't think presents are important. I will be more than
happy if you all come to the party."

10 May

Getting excited

Although Trumpeter had decided to have a party just for fun, he still planned to have all the trimmings – streamers, balloons, lemonade and cake. He wanted candles on the cake too. He had invited all his friends for the afternoon. He wanted them all to play games and have lots of fun. Trumpeter got very excited. He could hardly wait for the party to begin. He kept looking at the clock. "Aren't they here yet?" he moaned.

11 May

The cake

Trumpeter loved parties, and particularly birthday cake. He would eat any type of cake – fruitcake with lots of fruit, cream cake with lots of cream, or chocolate cake with lots of chocolate. But Trumpeter's favourite cake was super marshmallow cake. Do you know what a super marshmallow cake is? It is a gigantic cake covered with fruit and cream and chocolates and, of course, lots and lots of marshmallows. Really it is three cakes in one – a chocolate fruit cream cake with marshmallows!

12 May

Blow!

Trumpeter prepared to blow out the candles on his cake. He took a deep, deep, deep breath, closed his eyes and blew as hard as he could. Phooooosh! Very slowly, he opened his eyes. Had he blown out all the candles? He stared at the cake. He was shocked. There was hardly anything left! All the candles, cream, fruit and chocolate had disappeared! Trumpeter had blown all the nicest bits off the cake.

13 May

Fancy cakes

Trumpeter was cross. His lovely cake was ruined. He had closed his eyes and blew as hard as he could for just a few seconds and he was left with just a few crumbs. He looked at his friends. Henry Hare had got chocolate in his ears. Peter Peacock had got cream in his tail feathers. Porker Pig was covered in fruit, and Max Mouse was a pile of marshmallows! Trumpeter burst out laughing. "I blew so hard that I didn't just blow out the candles. I turned you all into fancy cakes." Luckily Max, Peter, Porker and Henry thought it was funny too.

95

14 May

Everyday parties

"Hey, Trumpeter, don't look so sad! Has something
happened?" Porker Pig asked his elephant friend.
Trumpeter shrugged his shoulders. He didn't answer;
instead he just let out a huge sigh. Porker began to worry.
Trumpeter was usually so jolly.
"Come on, let's go and sit down on a bench together,"
said Porker, "and then you can tell me why you are so sad."
Sitting on the bench, Trumpeter told Porker what was wrong.
"I like parties better than anything else in the world.
I'd like to have a party every single day. But if you have
a party every day, then after a while it's no fun any more.
I don't know what to do about it."

15 May

Help from Porker

Porker Pig stroked Trumpeter's trunk.
"You silly elephant," he said.
"Nobody has a party every day. Just think,
who would do all the work?"
Trumpeter sighed again. "But parties
are such fun," he said.
"I know," agreed Porker. "But if there isn't
a party going on, you can think about one.
Why don't you think for a couple of days
about a really marvellous party. The best,
the biggest and the most adventurous party
in the world. If it's a really good idea,
I'll help you organise it."

16 May

A party

I'm thinking of having a party,
The most colourful party you've seen,
With balloons and streamers and presents,
All party-goers must be keen!

We'll have a great time at this party,
We'll sing songs and play music all day,
With cymbals and drums and trumpets,
It's the best party yet all will say.

17 May

Being serious

"Are parties all you can think about Trumpeter?" asked Roy Rooster.
"There are serious things in life too you know."
"Ah well, I don't really like serious things," said Trumpeter. "I prefer to look on the bright side of life."
Roy Rooster didn't give up. "But you must know that the sun can't shine all the time. Sometimes it rains," said Roy, with a serious expression on his face. "Then I'll just have to have a rain party!" laughed Trumpeter.

18 May

The rain party

Roy Rooster had given Trumpeter an idea. He decided to have a rain party just for a change. He wouldn't need any paper streamers. They would get spoiled in the rain. No, what Trumpeter needed was a field, a good, muddy field, some elephant friends, and ... rain, of course!

Mud pies

Trumpeter looked at the sky with excitement. He saw a lot of grey clouds. It looked like it was beginning to rain. Drip, drip, drip. "Hurrah!" thought Trumpeter. "Now it's time for the rain party." Trumpeter and his elephant friends danced about in the rain. They thought it was wonderful. They splashed around in the puddles and in no time at all they were covered in mud from head to foot. "What an excellent party Trumpeter!" the other elephants shouted. "All this stamping about is making me hungry," giggled one of them. "Haven't you got any pies?" "Only mud pies!" said Trumpeter, and he threw a lump of mud at him.

The party hat

Porker Pig was going to visit his friend Trumpeter. As he walked along, he noticed something hanging on a bush. It was a hat. A lovely woollen hat. A hat that had been knitted by a very clever grandma, because it was knitted in different colours and it had tassels on it. Porker put on the hat and carried on to Trumpeter's. "Hello Porker," said Trumpeter. "What a lovely hat you're wearing." "Yes, isn't it? I found it." "But if you found it, that means someone must have lost it. A child perhaps. And that child will be really upset. Come on, let's go and see if we can find out whose it is."

21 May

A great big kiss

Porker Pig hoped that they wouldn't find the child and then he could keep the hat for himself. Then they heard someone crying. A little girl was sitting under a big tree with huge tears streaming down her face.
"What's the matter? Have you lost something?" asked Trumpeter.
"Yes, my lovely hat!" sniffed the little girl.
"Is this the one?" Trumpeter held out the hat.
"Yes it is. Oh where did you find it? Thank you so much." The little girl gave both Porker and Trumpeter a great big kiss!

A reward

Because Porker and Trumpeter had found the little girl's hat, she invited them home with her to have a glass of lemonade. There were two ladies in the little girl's house, a young lady and an old lady, and they were waiting for her to come home.

"Did you find your hat Becky?" asked the old lady.

"Yes Grandma, thanks to my two new friends, Porker and Trumpeter," said Becky.

"You have been very kind to Becky. I think you deserve a reward," said Grandma. "What would you like?"

Porker and Trumpeter looked at each other. They knew exactly what they would like.

"A lovely hat just like Becky's," they both said.

Party animals

Because Trumpeter was so cheerful, he had lots of friends. He was very popular. But his best friend was Porker Pig. "Why do you think we are such good friends?" Trumpeter asked Porker one day. Porker thought about this for a moment and then said, "I think it's because we both like parties. You are a real party elephant."
"Yes," laughed Trumpeter, "and you're the biggest party pig in the world!"

Henry Hare's party

Trumpeter the party elephant and Porker the party pig were walking through the park. Trumpeter felt a tap on his shoulder. It was Henry Hare. He said, "I bet you'd both like to come to a party."
"Yes please, we'd love to," answered Porker and Trumpeter.
"Then would you like to come to my house this afternoon? It's my wife's birthday and I want to surprise her with a very special party. I'm sure it will be great fun. See you this afternoon?"
"Yes Henry. We'll see you this afternoon!"

Party masks

Porker and Trumpeter were getting ready for the party, which would start in about two hours.
"What shall I wear?" cried Porker Pig.
"I don't know Porker. I don't know what to wear either!" said Trumpeter.
The two friends stood in front of the mirror for the next half an hour, trying on silly hats and pulling funny faces. But they didn't feel happy.
"Let's go to the fancy-dress shop," said Porker.
"They sell lots of funny masks and false noses."
"What a good idea," agreed Trumpeter.
The man in the fancy-dress shop laughed at Trumpeter and Porker.
"Silly billies," he said. "You two don't need masks. You look funny enough as it is!"

103

26 May

In bed

Trumpeter was ill. He was coughing a lot and he had a fever.
So he had to stay in bed.
Porker Pig came to visit him.
"How do you feel?" asked Porker.
"Awful," answered Trumpeter.
"That bad? Really?"
"Well, not *that* bad," admitted Trumpeter. "But it's no fun having to
lie in bed all day. I'm so bored."
Porker understood. "I have an idea," he said. "We'll have a party.
I'll invite all our friends. I'll tell them to bring their sleeping bags and
their pyjamas. Then we'll all sleep over at your house."
"I'm starting to feel better already!" said Trumpeter.

27 May

Pyjama party

"Trumpeter and I are having a pyjama party," Porker Pig told Peter Peacock. "Would you like to come?"

Peter frowned. "But I thought Trumpeter was ill?"

"That's why we're having a party," explained Porker. "It means Trumpeter can stay in bed and still have fun."

Peter wasn't very sure about this idea. He scratched his head. "Are you sure Trumpeter's illness isn't infectious?" he asked.

"Oh no!" laughed Porker. "He's got something that only elephants get. We can't catch it."

"Oh well, in that case," said Peter. "I'd love to come to your pyjama party."

28 May

A brave mouse

Trumpeter's bedroom was bursting at the seams. Porker Pig was there. So were Max Mouse, Peter Peacock and Henry Hare. They were all staying for the night and had brought their own sleeping bags.

"My sleeping bag is just like a burrow," said Henry Hare. "I can creep right down to the bottom." Henry's sleeping bag was padded and very warm. But Max Mouse had the most unusual sleeping bag. On it was embroidered a big black cat.

"Isn't it great?" said Max. "I'm the only mouse in the world that dares to sleep right next to a cat!"

29 May

The music shop

Next door to Trumpeter's house was a music shop. There were all sorts of musical instruments there. One day, the owner rung Trumpeter's doorbell. "Trumpeter," he asked, "could you help me? I've got to go away for a day on business. Would you look after my shop for me?"
"With pleasure!" replied Trumpeter.
"Would you like me to sell things too?"
"Of course. There is a price ticket on each instrument," said the owner.
"Here is the key for the shop.
Good luck Trumpeter!"

30 May

Sold out

At first Trumpeter had liked the idea of running a shop for a day. But not a single customer has been in all morning and Trumpeter thought running a shop was extremely boring. He decided to take some action. He hung a drum round his neck, put a tambourine on his head, held a trumpet in his trunk and went outside. Trumpeter started to bang the drum, rattle the tambourine and blow on the trumpet. He was a one-man band. The passers-by thought he was marvellous. They all wanted to join in. So they all rushed into the shop to buy an instrument!
When Trumpeter's neighbour returned from his business trip that evening, his shop was nearly empty. Trumpeter had sold almost all the instruments!

106

31 May

Making music

Although I'm just an elephant,
I'm musical you see,
I love the flute, the harp, the drum,
I play them – one, two, three!

I play them in the kitchen,
I play them in the hall,
But underneath my bedclothes
Is the quietest place of all.

107

1 June

Benny

It was a beautiful summer's day. The sun was shining and the birds were singing their hearts out. All the children were playing outside. So was Benny. Benny was a happy little boy, and he had lots of friends. When the weather was fine, Benny liked to play outside. He loved to ride on his bicycle and in his pedal-car and he completely forgot about all his other toys. He left those in his room, lying around on the floor.

2 June

Olly Bolly

When it rained, Benny played in his room. He had lots of toys.
He had a wooden train set, which he set up in his room.
He had a harlequin puppet with a pointed red nose.
Then there was Grumbly Bear, who really did grumble when Benny pressed his tummy. But Olly Bolly was Benny's favourite toy.
Olly Bolly was a soft, cuddly patchwork elephant with great big pink ears and a lovely long trunk.

Benny's baby sister

When Benny was only three, his mother had a very big tummy. A baby was growing inside her tummy. The baby was Benny's little sister. But Benny didn't know that then. One day, Benny's mother didn't feel very well and she had to go to hospital. Benny went to stay with Grandma. Benny's mother had to lie very still in bed in the hospital, which was very boring, and she began to miss her little Benny. So she made him a soft, cuddly elephant from lots of pieces of material. A few weeks later she came home, with Benny's little sister and with Olly Bolly, the cuddly elephant. So that was why Benny thought that Olly Bolly had been born in hospital.

4 June

Cuddly elephant

Olly Bolly, the cuddly elephant,
Squeeze and hold him tight.
Benny loves him oh so much,
He'll hug him through the night.

110

5 June

Big ears

Benny took Olly Bolly everywhere - to the shops, to school, to the sandpit, and at night Benny took him to bed. Benny adored Olly Bolly. But Olly had one small problem, he couldn't stand up. Every time Benny put him down, he fell over on to his trunk. Benny couldn't understand it.
"Why does he keep falling over?" he asked.
"Because Olly Bolly is top-heavy," explained his mother. "His ears are too big."

6 June

Olly's new tail

Benny felt sorry for Olly Bolly because he kept falling over. He looked very closely at his cuddly elephant.
"Do you know something Olly Bolly? Elephants are unusual animals. They have a big head with big ears and a long trunk. But that's all at the front. There's hardly anything at the back, just a tiny little tail. So I've made you a lovely long tail!"
Benny held up a long string of beads and then fastened them to Olly Bolly's tail. Olly could stand up!

Lonely Olly Bolly

Benny was playing outside with his bicycle and his pedal-car. Olly Bolly wasn't allowed outside because Benny was afraid that his friends would laugh at him. Olly was lonely. Huge tears rolled down his trunk. "It's not fair!" grumbled Grumbly Bear. "Benny always forgets about us when it's nice weather."
"I know," sniffed Olly.
"Don't worry about Benny!" laughed Harry Harlequin, jumping up and down. The bells on his hat tinkled. "Let's have fun ourselves!"

Playing by themselves

"If Benny won't play with us, then we'll play by ourselves!" cried Harry Harlequin. Harry wanted to cheer up the other toys.
"Yes, that's a great idea!" cried Olly Bolly. "Let's play with the train set."
Even Grumbly Bear got excited when he thought about playing with all those trains. "That could be fun," he said, picking up part of the railway track. They decided to build a really long track.

9 June

The toy train

Olly Bolly was feeling hot. He had been carrying parts of the train track around all morning with his trunk. Grumbly Bear and Harry Harlequin had joined the track together. The railway track ran all over the bedroom - under Benny's bed, past the toy chest and over to the window where Grumbly Bear had built a station out of wooden blocks.

Then the great moment arrived; they put the engine and three carriages on the track. Off they went, Olly in the first carriage, Grumbly Bear in the second and Harry in the third. Choo Choo!

10 June

Benny comes back

Olly Bolly, Grumbly Bear and Harry Harlequin had built an excellent railway. The train raced through Benny's room. Olly, Grumbly and Harry were enjoying themselves so much that they forget about Benny. He had finished playing outside.
He opened the door ...
"Hey, what's going on?" he cried with amazement.
His eyes opened wide.
Olly, Grumbly and Harry sat absolutely still. Toys weren't supposed to be able to play by themselves!

113

11 June

Did I dream?

Did I dream that Olly built a
railway track?
Did I dream it went around the
room and back?
Did I dream I heard a crash?
Did I dream he'd had a smash?
Did I dream he'd hit the wall?
Did I dream he'd had a fall?

12 June

Olly is allowed out too

Benny was playing outside with Jack and Emma, the children
who lived next door. Suddenly, Emma let go of her bicycle.
"Oh no!" she shouted. "I've got to give Suzy her bottle."
She ran inside to get Suzy, her doll. It made Benny
think about Olly Bolly.
"I've got to get my elephant," he said
casually. He didn't want
Jack to laugh at him.
 "Then I'm going to get my rabbit!"
said Jack. "Oh good," thought Benny,
"Olly will be able to play too."

114

13 June

Together in the pedal-car

"Come on Olly!" said Benny to his cuddly elephant. He picked up Olly by his trunk and dragged him downstairs. Bumper-debumper-debump down all those stairs. He banged his elephant bottom on every step. "Ow! Ow! Ow!" he shouted, but Benny didn't hear him.

"Come on, we're both going in the pedal-car," cried Benny excitedly. Outside on the pavement was a beautiful red pedal-car. It was Benny's birthday present from Grandpa. Benny jumped in behind the wheel and propped up Olly behind him.

"Ow!" said Olly again. "Right. We're nice and comfortable now, so we're all set," said Benny.

Vrooom! Off they drove. Even Olly enjoyed himself!

14 June

Drive

We drive all around
In my beautiful car,
New places we've found
As we've travelled near and far.
The sun in the sky
And the wind in my face,
Today is a day
I would never replace.

115

Picnic

"Are you coming?" asked Benny's mother. There was
a big basket on the draining board. Benny stood in
the middle of the kitchen with Olly Bolly under his
arm. "Olly wants to know what's in the basket first,"
said Benny.
"It's a surprise, so I can't tell you!" she answered.
Later on they went for a walk in the park. Mother stopped
when she came to a grassy patch covered with daisies.
"This is a nice spot," she said.
"Why have we stopped here?" asked Benny.
"Olly can look in the basket now," answered his
mother, "because this is a good place for a picnic."
Olly realised then what was in the basket,
and so did Benny.

A lovely dream

That night Olly had a lovely dream. He dreamt that he went for a delicious picnic with his friends Grumbly Bear, Benny and Harry Harlequin. Benny's mother had filled the basket with lots of wonderful things to eat. "Mmm, just look!" called Harry. "Lovely lollipops!" "Yuk, I don't like lollipops!" grumbled Grumbly Bear. "I'd much rather have a jar of honey."
Benny ate cake. But what do you think Olly ate? Olly ate red and green apples. He loved apples.

17 June

Nice warm bed

Benny took only Olly Bolly the elephant to bed with him. Benny slept best with Olly next to him. Olly was quite happy about this, but he did feel a bit sorry for the other toys.
One morning he woke up before Benny. He crept out of bed as quietly as he could. "Psst! Grumbly, Harry!" he called softly. "Come on into bed too!"
Grumbly and Harry Harlequin were delighted and jumped up into the nice warm bed. When Benny woke up a bit later, he said in a surprised voice, "But I thought I had only dreamed that you were all in bed with me!"

18 June

A new toy elephant

Aunt Sheila was coming to visit. Aunt Sheila always brought Benny a present. Benny watched at the window, clutching Olly Bolly under his arm. "She's taking a long time," he sighed.
After what seemed like hours, he saw Aunt Sheila's car. She got out and waved to Benny. In the sitting room, Auntie Sheila teased Benny. "Dear me, I don't think I've brought anything for Benny with me this time." When she saw the disappointed look on his face, she laughed and said, "Oh yes, silly me. I have remembered Benny's present after all!" She pulled out a big box from her bag. Benny ripped off the paper. It was an elephant. Another elephant! But this one was wooden, and it was on wheels.

19 June

Clangle, the elephant on wheels

It was a lovely present. Benny had never seen anything like it before. The elephant was beautifully painted, with a long red cord to pull him along. Benny tried it out straightaway. Lots of little bells tinkled as the elephant rolled along.
Benny was thrilled with his new elephant. "Thank you very much Aunt Sheila," he beamed. "I'm going to call this elephant Clangle!"

118

20 June

Jealous

Olly Bolly was sulking in a corner of the room,
where Benny had dropped him.
Benny didn't notice Olly, because he was happily
playing with Clangle, his new elephant on wheels.
He pulled him up and down the room. Then he ran
round the room. Clangle's bells tinkled even more.
Olly Bolly was not happy.
He thought that Benny would never play with him again.
He would show that Clangle, he thought to himself.

21 June

Jingle jangle

Jingle jangle
There goes Clangle,
An elephant on wheels.
He's made of wood
Which isn't good
If he treads upon your heels.
Jingle jangle
There goes Clangle,
An elephant on wheels.

22 June

Bedtime

Benny had played with Clangle all afternoon.
"Hurry up and go to bed," said his father. "Then we can have a bit of peace
and quiet without those annoying bells ringing all the time."
"Can Clangle come to bed with me too?" asked Benny.
Olly Bolly was still lying in a corner of Benny's room, where
Benny had left him. He couldn't believe what he heard ...
Benny wanted to take Clangle to bed, and not him!
Olly thought Benny was being so unkind.
He was really upset.

23 June

Remember Olly

Benny's father didn't think it was a good idea
to take Clangle to bed. "But Benny, Clangle is
made of wood. Just feel how hard he is,"
said his father.
"Oh, please," begged Benny.
"Absolutely not," said his father. "Clangle is a
hard wooden elephant, not a cuddly elephant.
Look at poor Olly Bolly!"
Benny glanced across to Olly lying there in the
corner. He went over and picked him up.
"Oh Olly, my best friend! I almost forgot
about you!" he said and hugged him tightly.
"You're lovely and soft."
Benny and Olly snuggled down in bed. And
what happened to Clangle? It was his turn to
stand in the corner of the bedroom.

24 June

All night long

You're so lovely and soft,
And you keep me so warm,
All night long.

With your head on my arm,
I can feel your soft ears,
All night long.

When I close my eyes tight,
I feel nice and tired,
All night long.

Then I sleep and I dream,
And you sleep and you dream,
All night long!

Night Night, Sweet Dreams
Olly Bolly!

25 June

In the middle of the night

Benny was soundly sleeping, but Olly was wide awake.
His shiny button eyes watched the shadows the trees made on the wallpaper.
He thought about Clangle. Wooden Clangle. Brightly painted Clangle.
Very noisy Clangle. Clangle who played with Benny all day long.
Olly didn't like him. "Psst!" Olly looked down. It was Clangle. "Can't you
sleep either?" he asked Olly. "No," mumbled Olly. "I don't like it when
Benny ignores you, you know," said Clangle. Olly was quite surprised
to hear this. When Clangle suggested that they should play with
Benny together, Olly thought that perhaps
Clangle wasn't so bad after all.

26 June

To the sandpit

The next morning Benny took both his elephants to the sandpit. He held
Olly Bolly safely under one arm and pulled Clangle along behind him.
The bells tinkled.
In the sandpit Benny had a big tipper truck, a spade and lots of different
buckets. First he put Olly and Clangle safely on the edge of the sandpit,
in the sunshine. "There you are, now you can watch!" said Benny.
Then Benny started digging He didn't stop. He was building
a big castle with a deep moat around it.

27 June

Don't forget us!

Olly and Clangle watched Benny as his castle took shape.
"Phew, isn't it warm?" puffed Olly.
"And we're not even doing anything," complained Clangle.
"I want to play too."
"Yes, let's," agreed Olly. "Benny will never notice
if we jump down into the sandpit."
Olly grabbed hold of Clangle's string and
flung himself forward into the sand.
Clangle's bells tinkled a little bit,
but Benny didn't notice.
Olly and Clangle giggled
and started to dig.
They were building
their own
sandcastle.

Sandcastles

Benny hadn't noticed the two sneaky elephants building their own sandcastle. Olly and Clangle wanted to surprise him.
All three of them were concentrating hard.
Benny was building a big castle, Olly and Clangle a small one.
Olly decided to dig a deep moat with his trunk.
There was a lot of sand to move and so he had to keep digging.
He was working so hard that his ears were no longer pink, they had turned bright red! Olly fell backwards because he was so tired and, by accident, knocked over one of the walls of Benny's castle. "Hey," Benny cried.
"Who did that? Oh Olly, you silly thing!
Why don't you ever watch what you're doing?
You've just fallen right off the wall onto my sandcastle. Just look what you've done!"
Benny was so cross that he didn't even notice the castle the elephants had made.

29 June

In the bath

Olly Bolly, Benny and Clangle were covered
in sand. Benny's mother shrieked when she
saw them. "Outside, the lot of you!" She took off
Benny's clothes and put them straight into the washing
machine. Then she got the garden hose. "It's lucky the
weather is fine," she said and turned on the tap.
Benny screamed. "Olly and Clangle too! Not just me!"
he shouted.
His mother then turned the hose on them. They loved
it. When all the sand had been washed off, Benny's
mother got a big towel and rubbed Benny, Olly and
Clangle dry.
"Now that you're all clean, it's time for something nice
to eat," said Benny's mother. Benny and the elephants
sat down on the towel with their nice juicy apples.

30 June

Sand everywhere

I've come out of the sandpit,
And oh, what a mess,
There's sand in my hanky,
And sand in my toes,
And even sand on the end of my nose.
There's sand in my trousers,
And sand in my shirt,
And sand in my eyes
And it's starting to hurt.
There's sand in my pockets,
My shoes, and my hair,
More and more sand, sand everywhere!

1 July

A greedy elephant

What was that huge pink mound lying in the middle
of the flowers in the field?
It looked like a tummy, but could a tummy be that huge? It was a
tummy though; it was Tubby's tummy. Tubby was a small, round
elephant. And the reason why he was so plump was because he
loved sweet things. He liked liquorice, toffees and lollipops. But his
favourite sweet was chocolate.
Tubby was dozing in the sun. His pink tummy felt nice and warm.
He was smiling. He was probably dreaming about chocolate bars!

2 July

Grandma

Tubby the little plump elephant was going to visit his grandma.
Grandma lived on the other side of the forest.
"Are you ready Tubby?" asked his mother. "Yes I am. I can't wait. I love
going to Grandma's," shouted Tubby. Mother elephant smiled. She knew
why Tubby liked visiting his grandma so much. Grandma had got a
large tin. A large, round tin with a shiny lid. And inside the tin were ...
chocolates! Grandma had told her that there would be something in
the tin that Tubby would like.

3 July

Chocolate

It's brown, it's hard, it's very sweet,
It's chocolate, and it's nice to eat.

Now guess what puts Tubby in a good mood?
It's chocolate, not really any other food.

How did his tummy get so big?
From too much chocolate – greedy pig!

4 July

The lollipop tree

Tubby had a big sister. Just like all big sisters, she sometimes
teased her little brother, especially with sweet things. She told
Tubby that there was a lollipop tree in the middle of the forest.
"That's not true! I've never seen it!" said Tubby angrily.
"It only flowers once a year," his sister replied. "But when
it does, it's full of lollipops. I'd go and have a look today
if I were you."
Tubby didn't know whether to believe her or not. He decided
to go to the forest and search for the lollipop tree, but, of
course, he didn't find it. Feeling very tired, he trudged home.
He was determined to get his own back on his sister.

The lemon-drop factory

Tubby had thought of a plan. He would show his sister once and for all. She always teased him about his sweet tooth, but she had a sweet tooth herself. Early one morning, he opened his sister's bedroom door and said, "Get up! Father and Mother are taking us to the lemon-drop factory today. Quick. Get a move on!"

His sister leapt out of bed. What an excellent idea! She had to get ready quickly. She wondered why Tubby was laughing at her. "Ha, ha, ha! I'm only joking!" cried Tubby.

His sister was really mad and upset. She had jumped out of bed for nothing. Tubby gave her a piece of chocolate to make her feel better.

Ice cream

Tubby could hear the ice-cream van getting nearer and nearer. He always recognised the van's tune. As fast as his elephant legs would carry him, Tubby ran to his mother.

"Mother, please may I have an ice-cream?" he pleaded.

"We haven't got any left Tubby," said his mother.

"The ice-cream van is here. Oh please, please may I have one?"

Luckily for Tubby, his mother also wanted an ice cream. She grabbed her purse and they walked to the ice-cream van together. Tubby thought about which flavour he wanted, but eventually he chose chocolate, his favourite. Mother chose mocha, which tasted a bit like coffee and chocolate mixed together. Then she bought a raspberry ice cream for Tubby's sister. "Poor Father. He's got to go to work and so he misses out on our ice-cream treats," said Tubby.

7 July

Packing a suitcase

Tubby was looking forward to going on holiday. Mother elephant was busy packing.
Tubby had his own suitcase. His mother said that he could pack it by himself.
A little later, his mother went to Tubby's room to see how he was getting on.
Where was he? He wasn't in his bedroom, he wasn't downstairs. Then she heard a
sound from the cellar. She walked down to the cellar to see what the noise was.
There was Tubby. He had packed his suitcase full of chocolate bars.
"But Tubby," sighed his mother, "you should have packed clothes and a cuddly
toy in your case, not chocolate!"
Tubby didn't agree. She had said he could pack his own case after all, hadn't she!

8 July

On holiday

Tubby woke up very early. It was the
big day. The whole family was going on
holiday. All the suitcases were ready.
Father carried the tent, mother had two
suitcases, and Tubby and his sister each
had their own cases. Father went first,
then Mother, then his sister and
then Tubby. Mother got hold of
father's tail with her trunk, Tubby's sister
got hold of her mother's tail, and
Tubby grabbed his sister's tail.
"Tarantara," trumpeted father.
"We're off!"
They set off. It was a long walk, because
they had decided to go to the beach.

130

Camping

After a long journey, the elephant family arrived at the beach. Father chose a good spot under some trees and he started to put up the tent. It was a big tent and needed a few people to fix the ropes and tent pegs in place. But Tubby wasn't a bit interested in the tent. He only thought about the sea. He ran down to the water. It whooshed around his ankles. His sore feet felt so much better. He wanted to stay and paddle in the water for hours. But his mother said, "Come on Tubby, supper and then bed. You can go paddling another day."

Melted

Tubby had been very naughty. His mother had told him that he should put clothes and a toy in his suitcase, but he secretly stuffed some bars of chocolate in a corner. Tubby thought he would slip away quietly and eat them. But things didn't go quite as Tubby planned. The chocolate bars had melted in the hot sun. Inside his suitcase was a sticky brown mess. His clothes and his toy were covered in chocolate! His lovely red trousers were ruined. So Tubby wasn't able to sneak off and eat chocolate after all. He was so disappointed.

On the beach

Tubby had a good night's sleep in the tent. His father, mother and sister were still asleep when he woke up. He crept quietly out of the tent and walked along the beach. "Hey, that's strange. The sea was much closer yesterday," he muttered to himself. "Have you never heard of ebb and flood, low tide and high tide?" said a voice behind him. Tubby looked round and saw a small, pink piglet. "Hello, I'm Buffy. I'm here on holiday." "Hello, I'm Tubby and I'm here on holiday too." "Shall we be friends? I'll share my chocolate with you," said Buffy. Tubby knew right away that Buffy would be a great friend!

12 July

A new friend

"Mother, Mother, come and see. I've made a new friend. His name is Buffy." Tubby was very excited. Sleepily his mother looked out of the tent. She saw the piglet, who was just as chubby as her own son Tubby. When she looked at the two of them standing together, tummy to tummy, she thought how well matched they were. "Hello Buffy," she said. "You two go off and play together. But don't go in the water, and ... don't eat too much chocolate!"

Best friends

With a very best friend
You share a lot,
Sweets, secrets, toys,
Whatever you've got.

With a very best friend
You can play all day,
Then off to bed
And dream away.

Oh, so hot!

Tubby and Buffy the piglet, his new friend, were playing all sorts of games on the beach. They played with a beach ball, they ran, they played tag and football. Suddenly though, Buffy stopped playing. "Oh, isn't it hot!" he moaned. "It's making me feel dizzy." The piglet's pink face had turned quite white. Tubby wasn't sure how to help his friend. He didn't know whether to give him some chocolate, but that probably wouldn't do much good he thought. Then he had an idea. He rushed to the the sea, sucked up a trunkful of water and sprayed it all over poor Buffy like a shower. "Ooh, that's much better," sighed Buffy with relief.

Sunburnt

Tubby had been playing on the beach all day long. He had been having so much fun that he didn't notice how hot the sun was. His tummy began to itch. He wondered why.
"Mother, my tummy hurts!"
His mother looked at his tummy. It was very red. "Oh Tubby, you're sunburnt. Wait there and I'll rub some cream on your tummy to make it less sore."
She made sure Tubby was sitting in the shade and then she rubbed cream all over him. She gave him a piece of chocolate to make him feel better. Tubby forgot about the sunburn as soon as he had a piece of chocolate in his mouth!

16 July

The camp fire

"Mother, may I have some more chocolate?" asked Tubby, for what seemed like the hundredth time. "No Tubby, we'll be having supper in a minute." "But there aren't any pans on the cooker," Tubby protested. "That's because your father is making a camp fire this evening. We're going to have baked potatoes and perhaps some toasted marshmallows for dessert." "Oh good. Could my friend Buffy come too?" asked Tubby "Yes, of course he can. Go and get him," his mother replied. When the camp fire was hot and crackling, Tubby and Buffy put marshmallows on the ends of long sticks. They held them over the fire. When the marshmallows began to sizzle, they were ready to eat. They tasted wonderful.

17 July

Tubby's swimming trunks

It was a beautiful sunny day. The elephant family was going swimming. But where was Tubby? "Tubby, come on. We're going swimming!" yelled his sister. "I can't find my swimming trunks," said Tubby miserably. His mother went to have a look. Tubby was sitting in the tent holding his swimming trunks. "But you've got your swimming trunks right there. What's wrong?" asked Mother. Tubby burst into tears. "I'm so big. Everybody will laugh at me!" "Of course they won't, silly!" said his mother. "Elephants are supposed to be fat; it makes them very good swimmers." "Really Mother?" "Really Tubby."

Swimming

It was so lovely in the water. The whole family was splashing about in the sea. Tubby was having a marvellous time. He threw himself into the middle of the waves and dived underneath them.

"Be careful Tubby, don't go too far out," warned his mother. But Tubby wasn't listening. He was enjoying himself so much. He waded further and further out to sea. His mother felt a little anxious and wanted Tubby to come back towards the seashore. She had an idea.

"Who would like a piece of chocolate?" she called out loudly.

Tubby's ears pricked up at the mention of chocolate. He splashed and sploshed towards the shore as fast as he could. "Me, me!" he yelled.

Mother laughed. She knew he wouldn't be able to resist chocolate.

Underwater

Tubby loved being in the sea. He loved the sea almost as much as he loved chocolate. While he was tumbling about in the waves, he felt something hard under his feet. He wondered what it was. He put his head under the water to have a look. He had forgotten that he wouldn't be able to breathe underwater.

"Use your trunk, silly!" shouted his sister.

Tubby looked at her with surprise. He didn't know what she meant. "If you put your head underwater, but leave your trunk sticking up into the air then you can breathe normally," she explained. "You're an elephant, aren't you?"

What a good idea! He tried it. On the bottom of the sea, he saw a beautiful shell. He picked it up. He decided to take it home with him as a souvenir of his holiday.

20 July

The photograph

"Stand closer, smile, keep very still,
Wait for it – one, two, three,"
My father's taking photographs
Of the tent, of my friend, and of me.

Mother must be in it,
So must my sister too,
We mustn't forget anyone,
That simply would not do.

The photo will remind us
Of the sand and sea so wet,
And of a family holiday
We never will forget.

Rain

Tubby could hear the rain beating on the tent. He was disappointed because he knew it would be no fun on the beach in the rain. Buffy arrived after breakfast. He and Tubby sat together in the tent. Mother had noticed that the two of them were bored. So she took out a cloth and a large tin. "Right, boys, let's play the toffee game." Had they heard correctly? Toffee game? It seemed like a good suggestion. They took the toffees out of the tin and made a long snake with them on the cloth. Then they took turns to throw the dice. Whoever threw a three was allowed to take three toffees. When one of them threw a six, then he took six toffees. "Hurray!" shouted Buffy. He had thrown a six.

22 July

Goodbye Buffy

Little Tubby was sad. Buffy was leaving. His holiday had come to an end. The pig family had already packed everything, and Buffy and his parents came to say goodbye.
"You'll still be my best friend," Buffy said to Tubby.
"Yes, and you'll be mine too."
Tubby was close to tears.
"You can have my last bag of jelly babies as a goodbye present," said Buffy.
"Thank you Buffy. And I'll keep the last one until next year. Perhaps we'll meet up and I can give it to you then?"

A sand lollipop

Tubby's sister felt sorry for him because he was so sad and lonely since his friend had left. "I've got an idea," she said. "Let's build a sandcastle together." Tubby's face lit up. He rushed off to fetch his bucket and spade. "Let's see who can build the best sandcastle," his sister said. "Mother can decide who should be the winner." When they had finished, they called to their mother to come and choose a winner. She thought that Tubby's sister had built a lovely sandcastle and that Tubby's was a little strange. It looked like he had built a giant sand lollipop!

The end of the holiday

The holiday was over. They had packed their cases and taken down the tent. "Mother, may I have another jelly baby?" nagged Tubby. "No you may not. They're right down at the bottom of the case. I can't get them now." Tubby stomped off grumpily. At the beach he picked up a few shells and threw them into the sea. He really wanted to stay another week, but then he remembered about home, Grandma and Grandpa, and his friends. He hadn't seen them for such a long time. Perhaps going home wasn't so bad, he thought to himself.

25 July

Strawberry cake

On the way back home, the elephant family called in to see Aunt Anastasia, who was very proper.
"Tubby, make sure you behave properly, do you hear?" said his mother before they went inside. Tubby was dismayed at the thought of having to sit on a chair all afternoon and not being allowed to touch anything.
But Aunt Anastasia had a surprise in store for the elephants. She had made a big strawberry cake with lots of whipped cream.
Tubby ate his piece of cake very quickly, but Aunt Anastasia allowed him to have a second piece, and even a third! He had eaten far too much and soon fell asleep!

26 July

Home again

When they arrived home, Tubby realised how much he had missed his toys. He ran to his room, got them all out of his toy box and played quietly with them for hours. When his mother called, "Tubby, are you coming downstairs for a cup of tea? There are chocolate biscuits!" he didn't even hear her. His mother was surprised that he didn't rush downstairs and so she went to see what he was up to. When she saw him happily playing, she put a couple of biscuits on a plate and poured him a glass of lemonade. Handing them to Tubby she said, "There you are Tubby, you just carry on playing."

27 July

Toothache!

"Ow, ow, ow!" Tubby cried out. His cheek was red and swollen. The little elephant had got toothache. Mother telephoned the dentist. Luckily there was a free appointment later that morning. At the dentist's, Tubby climbed into a big chair. The dentist pressed a pedal and the chair gently tipped backwards. "Open wide Tubby. Then I can see inside your mouth. That's good," said the dentist. "I can see the problem," she went on, "you need a filling. Do you eat a lot of sweet things Tubby?" Tubby didn't answer, but blushed a little. "If you're a brave boy, I'll give you a treat afterwards," promised the dentist. "Chocolate?" asked Tubby hopefully. The dentist wasn't very happy with this suggestion. "Chocolate is very bad for your teeth you know. No, you'll get a nice new toothbrush."

28 July

No more chocolate

Since coming back from the dentist's, his mother had hidden all the chocolate bars. Tubby decided that it would be a good idea to visit Grandma, because she always had chocolate. He waved goodbye to his mother and walked over to Grandma's house. "Hello Grandma, I haven't eaten any chocolate all day," said Tubby. "I know," replied Grandma, "and I know why too! The dentist has forbidden you to eat chocolate hasn't she Tubby?" "Oh no," thought Tubby, "Grandma knows about the dentist." He was very disappointed. "But," laughed Grandma, "I've got another treat for you. A piggy bank. I'll give you five pence for each day you don't eat any chocolate."

141

29 July

Real tusks

Tubby looked at himself in the mirror.
He was proudly inspecting the
white pointy things that were sprouting
on both sides of his trunk.
"Those are tusks," his mother explained.
"If you look after them, they will
grow to be big and strong. But
you must brush them well
and stop eating chocolate."
After each meal, Tubby cleaned
his teeth and tusks. He brushed and
polished them until they gleamed.
Then he looked in the mirror again.
He was sure that his tusks had grown
a bit bigger already because of
all the brushing!

142

30 July

Eat sensibly

Little Tubby was growing big. He hardly
ever nagged his mother about chocolate.
Instead, he would take a big red apple from
the fruit bowl. His mother let him eat as much
fruit as he liked, because he always cleaned his teeth
after every meal. Mother was very proud of her son.
She really hadn't thought he could be so sensible and grown-up. He never asked for
a bar of chocolate anymore. Tubby felt pleased that his mother was proud of him.
He was actually proud of himself too.

31 July

Brushing your teeth

Thirty brushes up and down,
Clean the left side and the right.
This will make your dentist pleased
And keep teeth clean and white.

Thirty brushes at the sides,
At the front and at the back.
Promise not to eat sweet food,
And hardly ever have sweet snacks.

143

1 August

A real lady

Anastasia was the most sophisticated lady elephant you could ever imagine. She was so sophisticated, in fact, that her trunk had a double curl in it. She also had excellent manners. She never smacked her lips when she was eating and she always said please and thank you. She never got dirty and was always very polite. But she wasn't at all nice to the other elephants. She thought they were far too dirty and silly to talk to. Really though, she was rather silly herself, because the other elephants were really very nice.

2 August

The caterpillar

Anastasia Elephant was in her garden. She was admiring her lovely flowers. She loved the beautiful colours. But then she noticed a fat, brown caterpillar on one of the leaves.

"Bah, go away, dirty thing!" shouted Anastasia.

She tried to shake the caterpillar off the leaf.

"Hey, stop!" called out the caterpillar. "Why should I get off?"

"Because you're dirty and ugly. You're spoiling my whole garden."

"But don't you know that I'll turn into a beautiful butterfly, much prettier and more colourful than all the flowers in your garden?" answered the caterpillar.

3 August

A dream prince

Anastasia had a dream. A charming dream to go with a charming elephant. She dreamt that she was going to marry a real elephant prince. Then she was going to live with her prince in a beautiful palace. There must have been at least a hundred rooms in the palace. Anastasia could see herself as a princess. On her charming grey head she was wearing a small, golden crown. Not one of those big, heavy crowns with lots of glittering diamonds on them. No, a sweet, dainty golden crown.
It was so small that she even kept it on when she went to bed.

4 August

You are what you are

Oh, silly Anastasia!
What funny ideas you've got,
You are what you are, an elephant,
You can't be what you're not.

Oh, silly Anastasia!
You're so foolish, I have found,
You are what you are, an elephant,
Quite plump, and grey, and round.

146

5 August

Mirror

Anastasia's favourite place to sit was at the side of the lake. When there was no wind, the water in the lake was just like a huge mirror. She would sit and look at herself for hours on end. Paul Perch lived in the lake. He had often seen Anastasia and decided to go and talk to her. But when he poked his head out of the water, it made ripples on the surface. Anastasia was cross.
"Go away, horrible fish, you're ruining my mirror!" she snapped at him.
Paul Perch wasn't very impressed with her behaviour. He didn't think she was very friendly at all. The lake belonged to everyone, after all.

6 August

At the hairdresser's

Anastasia was on her way to the hairdresser's. She had read somewhere that all sophisticated and stylish ladies had their hair curled. So she picked up her handbag with her trunk and set off.
"But Anastasia," said the hairdresser, "you only got a few strands of hair on top of your head. There really aren't enough to make any curls!"

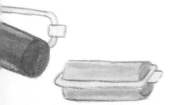

The picnic

It was such a beautiful day that Anastasia Elephant decided to go on a picnic. But it had to be a very sophisticated picnic. Into her picnic basket she put a tablecloth, plates, knives, forks, glasses and even real napkins. Then she put in some delicious things to eat and a bottle of fizzy lemonade. Together with her friend Henrietta Horse, she spread out the tablecloth on the grass underneath a large chestnut tree. They got out all the picnic things and slowly, with great care, sat down on the edges of the tablecloth. Suddenly Henrietta screamed, "Ow! We're sitting right on top of an ant hill!"

The two ladies ran away screaming and left the lovely picnic behind.

The ants were delighted and they didn't need the knives and forks!

8 August

Beauty sleep

Anastasia had a nap every afternoon. She told everybody that she was very tired. But that wasn't really true. She really went to bed for her beauty sleep. One day, she noticed that there were some wrinkles in her trunk. She was so shocked that she went to see Orry the owl to get his advice on what to do. Orry laughed. "Perhaps a beauty sleep might help," he said. But he didn't tell her that she had lots more wrinkles, and not just on her trunk!

Washing

Anastasia thought that most of the animals were rather dirty. They ate off the ground and rolled around in the sand and mud. They weren't suitable company for an elephant as sophisticated as Anastasia. But the raccoons were acceptable, just, to Anastasia. Their manners were nowhere near as good as her own, but at least they washed their food before they ate it. What Anastasia didn't know, however, was that the raccoons were not a bit impressed by good manners. They much preferred to roll around in the sand. But sshh, don't tell Anastasia!

10 August

Tarantara tarantara!

All the elephants were in a silly mood. They were running around chasing each other and making lots of noise. "Tarantara tarantara!" trumpeted the biggest elephant. "Tarantara tarantara!" trumpeted the others. It was just like a concert. They all joined in, except Anastasia, of course. She was far too refined to join in with these antics. What a noise they made! What awful trumpeting! Why couldn't elephants sing beautifully like the birds she thought? But Anastasia should have realised how strange that would sound – a great big elephant twittering like a little bird!

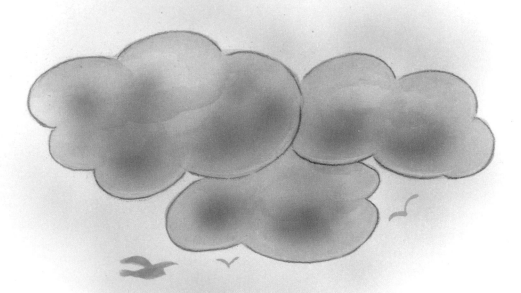

11 August

The raincloud

Anastasia was doing a little bit of gardening. A grey cloud
blocked out the sun.
"Pooh, nasty cloud," complained Anastasia, "you're spoiling my
whole day. You remind me that I'm grey and ugly too."
The cloud looked down at her. "Silly elephant, not
everybody thinks that grey is ugly. Look at the
plants and flowers. They know that I'm
going to water them with my
raindrops, so they're happy that
I'm a grey raincloud."

12 August

New neighbours

Anastasia had new neighbours. Father and Mother Hog and their nine children
had come to live next door. The children loved to play outside. They rooted around
in the mud with their snouts.
"It used to be such a nice neighbourhood," moaned Anastasia to her friend,
Henrietta Horse. "I'm thinking of moving."
But then the smallest hog gave Anastasia a bunch of flowers.
"These are for you, ma'am," he said politely. "Well, that's very nice of you,"
she said to the hog. She decided to wait and see before moving.

Flowers

Because you're so nice,
I'll give you
A big bouquet of
Flowers white and red.

Because you're so nice,
I'll give you
A big bouquet of
Flowers big and small.

151

14 August

Important visitors

Anastasia Elephant was so excited. King Lion was visiting the forest. She had tidied her whole house and baked a plateful of cakes. She was sure that King Lion would drop in and take tea with her. She was, after all, the most refined animal in the forest.

She could hear trumpets in the distance. King Lion was on his way. Anastasia waltzed outside to greet him. She had put on her prettiest dress. She waved to King Lion when he reached her door, but he just waved back and continued on his way. "Oh no!" she thought, "he is going to visit the Hog family. Well, that's his decision," thought Anastasia with a huff. And with that she scooped up all her lovely home-made cakes and munched them all in one great big mouthful. Anastasia didn't look so refined then did she?

15 August

Proud of a name

Anastasia was very proud of her name. None of the other animals in the wood had such a beautiful name.

Paul Perch or Sam Squirrel sounded very ordinary when compared to Anastasia. And the other elephants hardly had names that they could boast about - Dolly, Tubby, Olly and Bunter. No, Anastasia wouldn't have swapped her name with anyone. Anastasia could have been the name of a princess. It was such a shame that the other animals found her name far too difficult to pronounce. Do you know what they called her? Anna-tassie!

16 August

Red lumps all over

Anastasia had to go to the doctor's. "Oh, doctor! I've come out in red lumps all over. Is it some terrible disease?" she sobbed. The doctor examined the lumps closely and smiled. "No, no," she said. "These are mosquito bites. You're not ill at all." "So what can I do about them doctor?" asked Anastasia. The doctor answered with a smile, "The best cure for mosquito bites is a mud bath. That's what all the other elephants do." Anastasia turned bright red. She was horrified by the idea of sitting in a dirty old mud bath like all the other elephants!

Stop thief!

"Help, help! Stop thief!" screamed Anastasia. The other animals rushed
up to see what was happening.
"My bracelet has been stolen! It was in the drawer only this morning and now it's
gone! Thieves have stolen it!" wailed Anastasia.
"Do you know who stole it then?" asked Henrietta Horse.
"Those horrible Hogs of course! Who else? The dirty things haven't any
morals or manners at all."
"That isn't true. We're not thieves," said Father Hog angrily and walked off.
"Hmmm, hmmm," coughed Henrietta, "what's that on your front leg Anastasia?"
Anastasia looked down and blushed. There was the bracelet. That was why it
wasn't in the drawer. So would have to go and apologise to the Hogs, which
wouldn't be easy for her.

18 August

Queen of the Summer

All the animals in the forest
were happy. Everybody
was invited to a big fancy-dress party.
Sam Squirrel went as a Roman
soldier and Rupert Rhino as a police
officer. Clive Camel was wearing a
farmer's smock and Henrietta
Horse had transformed herself
into a witch. The last to arrive
was Anastasia.
She looked so beautiful,
dressed as the queen of the
summer, with a long pink veil
and a crown of flowers on her
head. All the animals agreed,
Anastasia was the most
charming queen of
the summer they
had ever seen.

19 August

Ballet

Anastasia thought that it was about time she took up a sport. But she wasn't sure which one to choose? Which sport was the most sophisticated? Horse-riding? But where would she find a horse that would carry an elephant? After a lot of thought, Anastasia decided on ballet. She had bought a pretty pink ballet dress with a pink bow to tie on her head. She jumped and spun round and round in time to the music. It felt wonderful. Anastasia was jumping around so enthusiastically that the ground quivered for miles and miles!

20 August

Miss Manners

Anastasia Elephant had a visitor. Her niece had come to see her. They were taking tea together. "Would you like a little cake with your tea Dorothea?" asked Anastasia. "Yes please," answered Dolly with a smile. "Shame on you!" scolded Anastasia. "Haven't you forgotten your manners? You must never say just 'yes' or 'no' to a grown-up elephant." Dolly looked at her aunt in amazement. She didn't understand. "But I didn't just say yes, I said 'yes please'."

21 August

A mouse

Elephants were the biggest animals in the forest. Because they were so big and strong, they weren't frightened of anybody. They always stood their ground.
Anastasia walked along with her trunk in the air.
She was so sophisticated that she never ran.
But something very unexpected happened. Anastasia started to run. "Help!" she screamed.
She had seen a mouse. She ran and ran, huffing and puffing as if her life depended on it.
What a funny sight – a great big elephant running away from a tiny mouse.

22 August

Table manners

Anastasia the elephant
Is quite the perfect guest.
Real ladies know their table manners,
Hers are the very best.

Always eat with knife and fork,
And never smack your lips,
Use your fork if eating meat,
And never spit out pips.

Do not finish all the biscuits,
Say politely "Thank you m'am",
Never ever mash potatoes,
Never, never say "More jam!"

23 August

The paper hat

Anastasia Elephant was walking in the forest. She was wearing a paper hat. Suddenly it began to rain and the wind started to blow. She held on to her hat with her trunk and started to walk faster. She wanted to get home. But the rain began to pour and the wind got stronger. Big raindrops fell on her lovely hat and it just collapsed. She took it off. A soggy pile of paper on her head didn't look very sophisticated at all!

24 August

Muddy heroine

Anastasia Elephant wasn't happy. She was the most sophisticated elephant in the forest, but the other elephants didn't seem to be interested in her at all. They didn't treat her with the respect she deserved, she thought to herself. Suddenly she heard a scream. She ran towards the scream and discovered a very small elephant who had fallen into a deep muddy hole. She didn't stop to think. With a giant leap, she jumped right into the hole and lifted the little one out. Phew, she had done it! She was covered in mud from her trunk to her tail. She felt so ashamed of the state she was in, she tried to slink away quietly before anyone would see her. Then she saw the other elephants. Too late, she thought. But they seemed to be looking at her with admiration. They were. They were so proud of the way she had reacted in saving the little elephant. Anastasia realised that she had done something very important. The mud had turned her into a muddy heroine!

157

25 August

Fibber!

Henrietta Horse had baked a large cake, a cake with lots of whipped cream.
Because it was far too big for her to eat on her own, she had invited her lady
friends round for cake and a cup of tea. Anastasia Elephant was invited.
They all sat at the table and admired the cake. It looked wonderful. Anastasia just
adored whipped cream. She couldn't help herself ... when nobody was looking,
she sneakily ate a cream rosette. Of course, Henrietta noticed that someone
had touched her lovely cake.
"Who has been pinching cream from the cake?" asked Henrietta crossly.
"Not me," answered all the ladies in turn.
"Not me," answered Anastasia.
Shame on you Anastasia. Sneaking cream secretly from the cake was not
very well-mannered, but fibbing was much, much worse!

26 August

Spectacles

Anastasia Elephant kept banging into things. She usually strolled through the forest in such a calm and dignified way. Anastasia was wearing something she didn't usually wear. It was a pair of spectacles.

Anastasia had decided that a pair of spectacles would make her look so much more refined. So she borrowed Norris Know-All's spectacles. But she didn't need to wear spectacles. In fact she couldn't see properly through the lenses. Everything looked very fuzzy. What a silly, vain elephant she was. She should have been pleased that her eyesight was perfect.

27 August

Cheeky monkey

Bunter Elephant was always getting into mischief. He had thought
up another practical joke. He waited for Anastasia Elephant and then
shouted, "Look out, a mouse!" Anastasia jumped up in the air with
fright. Then she noticed Bunter, rolling around with laughter.
She realised that she had fallen for his trick.
"You just wait, you cheeky monkey! I'll pay you back for this," she
shouted crossly. "I'm not a monkey, I'm an elephant," answered Bunter.
But he decided to run away quickly before she got too mad.

28 August

Anastasia's aunt

It was the birthday of one of Anastasia's aunts.
An extremely proper aunt. Perhaps that was why she
was Anastasia's favourite aunt. On the way to her
aunt's house, Anastasia fiddled with her handbag
and the bow on her head.
"I hope I look neat and tidy,"
she muttered. She was so
preoccupied with herself
that she didn't notice the
great big puddle in the
middle of the road. Splash!
She dropped her handbag.
Anastasia was covered in
mud. Poor Anastasia
didn't look quite so
neat and tidy
anymore!

29 August

Nail biting

Why was Anastasia Elephant wearing gloves? It looked very refined, of course, but it must have been so hot on such a warm, sunny day. Anastasia was, actually, much too hot. But she didn't dare take off her gloves. She didn't want others to see her nails. Because Anastasia, the sophisticated lady elephant, bit her nails! Those horrid, bitten stumps on the end of her fingers looked dreadful. Anastasia had to try her best and leave her nails alone. Then she wouldn't need to wear gloves.

Scratch, scratch

"I don't know what's wrong with me today," sighed Anastasia, "but I'm itchy all over. My tail tickles and so does my trunk, my ears itch and my back too. It's driving me mad." "If you've an itch, then scratch it," said Father Hog.
"Scratch!" cried out Anastasia. "I couldn't possibly."
"Well then, you'll have to have a mud bath," replied Father Hog.
But Anastasia didn't like the idea of mud baths. But oh, oh, she was so itchy! With a deep sigh, she decided to try the mud. Very carefully, she put one foot in the mud. She pulled back her trunk in a flash because the mud smelled so terrible. But then she carried on, because she was so itchy. Finally she sank into the cool, thick mud. It felt wonderful and soothing on her skin. Father Hog was right, mud was good for itchy skin.

31 August

Mud

Anastasia the lady elephant
Sat down in a puddle of mud.
"Oh my, oh my," she said to herself,
"I must say this feels rather good.
It's a bit of a shock to begin with,
But you find it's nice after a while,
It's cooler than I'd expected,"
She said to herself with a smile.
"It's lovely and soft and it's slippery,
And it makes you feel warm if you're cold,
And believe it or not it makes elephants clean,
At least that's what I've been told."

163

Dolly

Usually Dolly was the little elephant
walking a long way behind the herd of elephants.
Dolly was always late. For everything.
Because she was always in a dream. She forgot
all about the rest of the herd when she was
dreaming. Only when her mother called her,
she got a move on and caught up with the others.
When she had caught up, she began to dream again
and forgot to put one foot in front
of the other. "Come on Dolly!"
called her mother and gave her
a shove with her trunk.

2 September

Rainbow

After a heavy shower of rain, the sun came out.
A beautiful rainbow appeared on the horizon.
Dolly was sheltering under some trees
with the other elephants.
"Oooh, look at those lovely colours," she sighed.
"I wish I was beautifully coloured."
She closed her eyes and dreamed of elephants
in all the colours of the rainbow.

3 September

Bruises

Dolly could be easily recognised by her bruises. The little daydreaming elephant was covered in bruises. She was always daydreaming and didn't look where she was going. She banged into all sorts of things. Stones, branches, even great big trees. Luckily Dolly didn't walk very fast when she was daydreaming, so she had never really hurt herself. But her mother sometimes grumbled, "You do look a sorry picture with all those bruises Dolly. Try to look where you're going."

4 September

Daydreaming

There are day dreams and night dreams. People dream night dreams at night in their beds and only sometimes remember them the next morning when they wake up. People daydream in the daytime. They're not really asleep and they can remember what they have dreamed. Dolly, the dreamy elephant, preferred day dreams.
"They are much better," she said, "I can choose what I dream about, which means I never have nasty dreams. I always think about something nice."

5 September

Cloud stories

A little round elephant was lying in the grass. It was Dolly. She was watching the white clouds floating in the sky. They were all different shapes. Some looked like sheep, some like faces, and others were exactly like elephants. One of the clouds looked just like a ship, an enormous cloud ship sailing in the sky. "I wonder what it would be like to sail in that cloud ship," Dolly thought. "I would be so high up, I would be able to see all the different countries in the world." Dolly had lapsed into daydreamland again, dreaming the loveliest dreams about far-away places.

6 September

A magician?

Dolly had been dreaming again and she had completely lost the rest of the herd. There wasn't an elephant in sight. Dolly was a bit worried. Perhaps a wicked magician had come and turned all the other elephants into blades of grass! Dolly was frightened and she started to run. The magician might have been following her too! Luckily for Dolly, she found the other elephants standing in the shade of some trees. They had been waiting for her. "Oh Mother! I thought a wicked magician had made you all disappear."

167

7 September

Dreamland

Dolly the little elephant
Loves to dream and dream.
For Dolly the dreams all come quite true,
Though not all what they seem.

Silly dreams, strange dreams,
It doesn't matter which,
The dreams are all the better
If there is a nasty witch!

But if the dreams get too upsetting,
Or extremely scary,
Along comes someone very like
An elephant's good fairy!

8 September

Dreambox

"They must have left the dreambox open too
long in your case Dolly," her mother said quite
often to her daughter.
When Dolly asked what a dreambox was, her
mother just laughed.
Dolly imagined it to be a beautiful blue box, with
gold and silver stars on the outside. The box was full
to the brim with lovely dreams. They laid there in the
box like little pink clouds, waiting. They were waiting
for a child who couldn't sleep. Because only when a
child really couldn't fall asleep could he or she choose
one of the pink cloud dreams. But the child would
have forgotten everything the next morning.
Have you ever not been able to sleep? Perhaps you
have chosen a dream from the dreambox too?

9 September

I'll dream what I like

"I just don't understand you," said Bunter to Dolly.
"You're always dreaming. That's boring! Playing
games is much more fun. And football is best of all!"
Dolly shook her head. She didn't agree. "I like
football too," she said, "but I'm not very good at it.
That's why I prefer to dream about things. If I
dream about football, then I dream that I'm
the best footballer in the whole world."

169

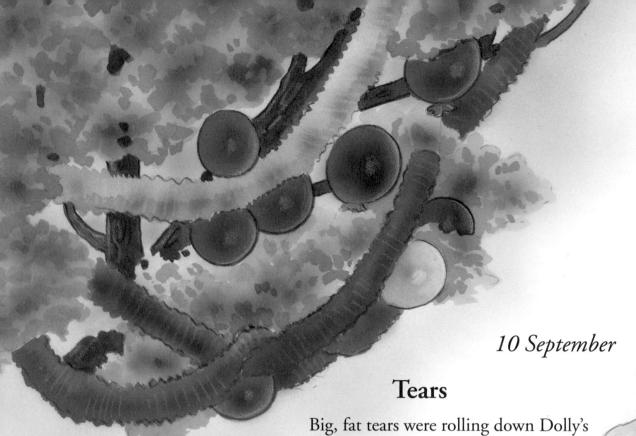

10 September

Tears

Big, fat tears were rolling down Dolly's
cheeks. "What is the matter?" asked her mother.
Dolly sniffed and had to swallow hard before she could
answer, "I dreamt last night that it was my birthday. I got lots
of presents and the whole forest was decorated with garlands."
"But that sounds lovely!" said her mother.
"Yes," sniffed Dolly, "but when I woke up this morning, everything was gone.
No presents, no garlands, nothing."
"Silly girl," said her mother. "Come here and have a great big hug."

11 September

A message

"Dolly," said her mother. "Will you take this basket of apples to your aunt?"
"Yes, of course," answered Dolly and set off. Her aunt lived a little way
away.
On the way, Dolly passed a field full of lovely flowers, which smelled
wonderful. The bees were buzzing round them. It must be lovely to fly
among the flowers, thought Dolly. She closed her eyes and dreamt that she
had a pair of beautiful transparent wings. Then she heard someone calling,
"Dolly, Dolly!" It was her aunt. Oh dear, all that daydreaming had
made her forget all about the basket of apples.

12 September

The cuddly toy

Dolly had a special cuddly toy.
She couldn't go to sleep without it.
"It's the best cuddly toy in all
the world," said Dolly.
"If I put my head on his hump
when I'm in bed, I dream the most
wonderful dreams."
Dolly's cuddly toy was a dromedary,
which is a camel with one hump.
But Dolly called him
her dreamedary!

13 September

Dreamedary

A genuine dreamedary
Is not found everywhere,
With pink legs and a purple face
They're very, very rare.

He's so cuddly to sleep with,
Though he looks extremely odd,
But this dreamedary takes me quickly
To the land of nod.

I won't swap him for a penguin,
Nor a great big cuddly bear,
For there are lots of bears and penguins,
A dreamedary is very rare!

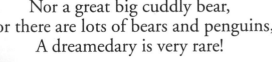

14 September

Blowing bubbles

Mother had given Dolly a bowl of soapy water. Very carefully, Dolly dipped the tip of her trunk into the water and sucked up a little. Then she blew gently through her trunk. She was making the most beautiful bubbles, in all the different colours of the rainbow. What a lovely game. Now Dolly could blow bubbles and dream at the same time!

15 September

Looking for Dolly

Mother elephant was looking for Dolly. "Have you seen Dolly anywhere?" she asked everyone. "No Mrs Elephant. But I expect she's daydreaming somewhere." "Yes, I suppose you're right," sighed her mother. "Dolly just doesn't look where she's going when she's daydreaming. I wouldn't be surprised if she were lost!" "Yoohoo!" There was Dolly. But why was her trunk purple? "Oh, mother, I've found some delicious blackberries. Come on, there are lots more!" Mother elephant followed Dolly. For once in her life, Dolly had actually kept her eyes open. The blackberries really were delicious.

16 September

The tramp

Dolly had never seen a tramp
before. The herd of elephants met
him as they were travelling through
the countryside. The tramp elephant
was all on his own and hadn't eaten
anything for days. The other
elephants felt sorry for him and so
they shared their food with him.
Dolly was dreaming again. She
dreamt that the tramp elephant was
really a prince. A wicked witch had
driven him away from his palace.
"There you are, Your Highness," she
said, as she handed him a sandwich. The
tramp elephant looked at her and was puzzled.
He didn't understand what she was talking
about. He didn't know Dolly and her daydreams.

17 September

Marbles

"Hey Dolly, are you coming to play marbles
with us?" asked the other elephant children.
"Wait a minute," she replied. She wanted to
count her marbles first. She emptied her
marble bag and saw that she had ten marbles
left. Nine small ones and one big one. The big
one shined so prettily in the sun. Dolly
wondered whether it could be a lucky marble.
 At the end of the game, Dolly counted her marbles
again. Now there were twenty. She had won ten.
So it must have been a lucky marble after all!

18 September

Short trunks

Dolly was sitting in the shade watching the other elephants.
She saw how they reached up to the highest leaves on the
trees with their trunks.
Dolly thought that trunks were such handy things
to have. If elephants had short trunks, they
would look so silly.
Dolly daydreamed about elephants with short
trunks. Then she laughed. She thought about
her father, who loved to eat fresh green
leaves. He wouldn't have been able to
pick them would he, if he
hadn't got a nice
long trunk?

19 September

An elephants' playground

"Guess what I'm dreaming about?" said Dolly. "I'm dreaming about a playground
specially for elephants. An ordinary playground is no good for us.
The swings are far too narrow for our big bottoms, and we're
much too heavy for the slide."
"So why don't you draw this playground of yours?" suggested her mother.
"What a good idea!" said Dolly and rushed to fetch her drawing pad.
It was going to be a wonderful playground, with great
big swings and a mound of sand as a slide. And, right
in the middle, there would be a big muddy pool.
Elephants liked playing with mud and water
more than anything else in the world.

Playground

The see-saw creaked and broke in two
A horrid crashing sound.
The swing was not much better,
For the ropes stretched to the ground.

For elephants in playgrounds
There is no place to hide,
Their grey gigantic bottoms
Break the see-saw, swing and slide!

21 September

Chicken pox

Dolly had a fever. She was covered with small, red, itchy spots.
"You've got chicken pox," her mother said. "You'll feel a bit poorly,
but it's not serious. You'll be better again in a few days.
But you mustn't scratch the spots, even if they do itch horribly.
If you do scratch, you'll be left with little holes in your skin."
A little later, Dolly managed to fall asleep.
She dreamt that she had been scratching
her spots. Her whole body was full of holes!
"Help!" she woke with a fright. "I'm leaking!" Mother then
explained that they weren't really holes, just scars.
But Dolly wasn't convinced. Just in case, she
put her arms under her pillow.

22 September

Getting better

Dolly thought that it wasn't so bad recovering from being ill. Her mother had brought her a big pile of books and a bowl of fruit. She felt warm and comfortable.

With her trunk under the covers, Dolly snoozed in her lovely soft bed. She could dream as much as she wanted, Dolly thought to herself.

But, try as she might, she couldn't dream. The dreams just wouldn't come! Dolly was worried that she might have run out of dream ideas and then she would have to go and find new ones in Dreamland. Dreamland could be miles away and she would have to travel by train, or through the desert, or perhaps over mountains ...

Dolly was off again, dreaming about a journey to Dreamland.

It seemed that her dreams hadn't run out, after all!

Portrait

Dolly Elephant liked visiting her Grandpa. His house was full of interesting things. Dolly particularly liked all the photographs he had. Among the pictures of Dolly's family were a few old photographs. One of them was a portrait of Great Uncle Solomon. Great Uncle Solomon had been a sailor. In the photograph he wore a captain's cap. If Dolly asked Grandpa really nicely, he told her all about the voyages that Great Uncle Solomon used to go on. At night in her bed, Dolly dreamed that she was sailing with Great Uncle Solomon on the oceans. They had the most marvellous adventures together. Dolly thought that it was a shame it was only a dream.

24 September

The wrong tail

Mother had an agreement with Dolly. "When we're out walking, you keep hold of my tail with your trunk. Then you won't get lost." So that's what Dolly did. She held on to her mother's tail tightly. Then she didn't have to concentrate on where to put her feet, so she was free to dream as much as she liked. They tramped through the forest together. Dolly's ear began to itch, so she gave it a good scratch with her trunk. Without looking, she searched for her mother's tail again. There it was! She tramped on through the forest and then looked up to her mother, but it wasn't her mother, it was a completely different elephant. She had grabbed hold of the wrong tail! It was a bit of a shock for Dolly. Luckily though, her mother had seen everything. She stroked poor Dolly's head. "Look what you're doing next time!"

177

25 September

The ball game

The elephant children were playing with a ball, throwing it to each other and catching it. They threw the ball harder and harder, but then, all of a sudden, the ball disappeared. They must have thrown it in the bushes. All the children started to search, except Dolly. Dolly was dreaming that she was a ball herself. She was thinking that if she were a ball, where would she roll to? Perhaps under that big bush with the lovely soft moss underneath. Dolly opened her eyes. She tramped over to the bush and looked underneath it. And there was the ball! The other elephants were so pleased with Dolly. They thought she was clever to find their ball so quickly.

26 September

Painted elephants

The other elephants had decided to play a trick on Dolly. They got a paintbox and some brushes and found a quiet place. They had decided to paint each other.
It didn't take them long. One elephant was purple with green hearts, another was blue with white flowers, and Bunter was yellow with black stripes, just like a tiger. They looked for Dolly.
"Yoohoo Dolly, are you coming to play?" they shouted, expecting her to be surprised. But Dolly wasn't a bit surprised. "Oh, aren't you beautiful!" she cried. "Just like in my dream. Will you paint me too?"
 They painted Dolly red with white spots. She looked like a giant toadstool with a trunk.

178

27 September

Dream princess

I dream I'm rich, as rich can be,
That I'm a dream princess,
With lots and lots of servants,
Well five or six, no less.
I live each day in a palace,
It's just a sleep away,
Mother and father live there too,
With parties every day!
There's chocolate ice-cream, yum yum yum,
And always chocolate cake,
And chocolate this and chocolate that,
My tummy starts to ache.
So when the party's over,
And my tummy's rather sore,
I open my eyes and wake up quick,
I'm a dream princess no more!

179

28 September

Princess Dorothea

Dolly's Aunt Anastasia didn't call Dolly just Dolly. No, she called her 'Dorothea'.
When Dolly visited her aunt, she always behaved beautifully. She said 'please'
and 'thank you'. She sat on her chair without fidgeting and didn't spill her
lemonade.
Can you guess how Dolly managed this? She simply dreamt that she was a princess.
And princesses always behaved beautifully. So her dreams were sometimes
useful after all!

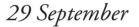

The treasure hunt

"Dolly, are you coming out to play?" asked the elephant children. "We're having a treasure hunt." Dolly thought that would be great fun. They might find some real treasure! Perhaps a chest full of gold coins and jewels. That would really be something. They would be very rich if they had a chest full of gold. Then they could buy anything they wanted – chocolate, toys, anything. Then Dolly saw the treasures the others had already found – a marble, a conker, some acorns and an old shoe. No, thank you very much, she thought, I'll carry on dreaming about my chest full of gold.

30 September

Elephant Dreamland

Dolly the little elephant
With her head in the clouds all day,
In her own Elephant Dreamland
She dreams the day away.

Dolly the little elephant
Believes her dreams are true,
In her own Elephant Dreamland
Her cares and worries are few.

1 October

The zoo

Have you ever been to the zoo? If you have, you will know all about the animals you can see there. Monkeys, bears, zebras, crocodiles, snakes, lions and tigers, not to mention the giraffes, ostriches and parrots. And elephants, of course!
I know a zoo that you have never visited. It is a very unusual zoo, because all the animals there can talk. All the children in the whole world want to go there.

2 October

Deedee

Deedee was a very special little elephant. She was very special indeed because she could talk. That's why she lived in the zoo for talking animals.
Deedee lived with her mother, father, sister, brother and Great Uncle Jumbo in a great big elephant park.
There were some old trees in the park, and some branches and tree stumps for the elephants to play with. People loved to visit the elephants. They fed them nuts and talked to them.
"Hello little elephant," they said to Deedee.
"What's your name?"
"Deedee," she answered, "what's yours?"

3 October

Uncle Jumbo

The funniest elephant in the zoo was Uncle Jumbo. He was always doing silly things
and he loved to tell jokes. He put on a real show if there were a lot of visitors. First, he
picked up a sturdy tree trunk and waved it about dangerously above his head. It was
a miracle that there had never been an accident. It was really frightening!
When everyone had recovered from the shock, he sung a jolly song.
The clever thing was that he could trumpet and sing at the same time!
Then he sat down and told a joke, usually the one about the mouse
and the elephant walking over a bridge ...

4 October

Animal day

It was Animal Day, and all the animals in the zoo were getting a special breakfast.
"Get a move on everybody! It's breakfast-time," cried Uncle Jumbo.
"Tarantara! Animal Day today. What a treat!"
Deedee had a quick wash at the lake, smoothed down her ears and went
to sit next to Uncle Jumbo.
Kevin the elephant-keeper was pushing a wheelbarrow
full of delicious things. Deedee could see bananas,
lettuces, loaves of bread ...
"Mmmm, may I have a loaf of white bread?" asked Deedee. "And I'll
have a bunch of bananas," said Uncle Jumbo, licking his lips.

5 October

Animal Day

All the animals dance and sing,
"Hurrah for Animal Day!"
With extra food and extra fun,
"Hurrah for Animal Day!"
They play, they trumpet and sing a song,
It's fun and games the whole day long,
And when it's time to go to their beds,
It's happy animal sleepy-heads.

6 October

Fun's over!

It had been so busy at the zoo. It seemed like all the grown-ups and children in the town had wanted to come and see the talking animals. All day long, Deedee and her brother Bouncer had been carrying branches and playing in front of the crowds. Kevin, their keeper, came to see them. "Look what I've brought you both for being such entertaining elephants," he said, "a present!" He threw a big red ball to Deedee. "Thank you!" shouted Deedee and Bouncer, thinking what a lovely change it would be from playing with branches. They played catch for the rest of the day. When the sun had almost set, their mother called, "Fun's over. Time for bed!"

7 October

Visitors

The elephant park was very nice, but not very big. The director of the zoo was planning to visit the park and she was bringing an engineer with her. He knew how to make and build things. They looked round the park.

"What do you think?" the director asked the engineer. "Do you think you can do anything with it? Make it a bit bigger and plant more trees and bushes?" The engineer scratched his head. "Yes that's no problem," he replied, "but I'd like to hear what the elephants themselves think. It is their park, after all." The elephants were so pleased to be asked and they gave some useful ideas to the engineer.

8 October

What would you like?

"I would like a big park with lots of places to hide," said Deedee. "And I would like a lake to swim in," said her mother. "A football pitch!" cried Bouncer. "I would like a large tree. Then I can lie down under it and go to sleep in the shade," said their father. "And I would like a rocky hill," said Uncle Jumbo, "to stand on when I tell a joke." All the elephants wanted different things in their new park, but did they all get what they wanted?

9 October

We would like a playground

We would like a playground,
A place for us to play,
With room enough for everyone,
Where we could stay all day.

Where we could run and jump and shout,
Where we could roll and fall about,
A running track, and water, trees,
Please try your hardest for us, please.

10 October

The new plan

The engineer listened to what
the elephants had to say. Then
he sat down at his drawing
board and thought, and
thought, and thought.
 At last, he picked up his pencils
and a large sheet of paper and
started to plan the park. At the
top he wrote the heading, 'Park
for the Elephant Family'.
That afternoon, he and the
director of the zoo went to
visit the elephants.
"Have a look at this," he said,
"I hope you like it!"

**11
October**

What
they all
want

The elephant family
studied the engineer's
plan. He had included an excellent rocky
hill for Uncle Jumbo and a lake for Mother.
There were large trees and a pergola for father,
which was an archway made from pieces of wood
along which plants could grow. Father would be able
to sit in the shade underneath. The engineer hadn't
forgotten Deedee and Bouncer, because he had
included a playground with goalposts and a giant
see-saw. There were bushes all the way round the
edge, which would be great for Deedee to hide in.
"It's brilliant!" shouted Deedee and Bouncer.
"Just what we all wanted," agreed
the other elephants.

12 October

Winter
home

It was getting colder at the zoo. "Brrr!"
shivered Uncle Jumbo. "Autumn is coming."
"We just can't get used to it," said Mother sadly.
She was thinking about the warm country
where she lived as a girl.
"Come now," said Father,
"it's nice here too. We'll be getting a
lovely new park very soon."
That was true. But the elephants had to
move to their winter home for a
little while. It was always nice and
warm there.

13 October

Moving

"Lady Elephants and Gentlemen Elephants," called Kevin. "Take your places in the line." It was time to move to their winter home. Uncle Jumbo stood at the front, because he was the oldest. Deedee and Bouncer were at the back.
"Grasp tails!" ordered Kevin. Bouncer got hold of Deedee's tail with his trunk, Deedee grabbed her mother's, mother took father's tail, and father firmly held Uncle Jumbo's tail. Uncle Jumbo hadn't got a tail to get hold of because he was the first in line.
"Tarantara tarantara!" he trumpeted. And off they marched, left, right, left, right, left, right ...

14 October

Left, right, left, right

Left, right, left, right,
Marching up and down,
Elephants marching single file,
Right across the town.

Left, right, left, right,
Stomping with their feet,
Happily they march along,
Keeping to the beat.

Left, right, left, right,
Stepping out together,
Merrily they march along,
Never mind the weather.

15 October

Their tropical home

In the middle of the zoo was a gigantic
building with tall doors and a glass roof.
This was going to be the winter home
of the elephant family once again.
They lived there every winter. Not
just the elephants, the chimpanzees,
crocodiles and tropical birds lived there
too. It was lovely and warm inside
and there were lots of tropical plants –
huge ferns and palm trees. It was a bit
like the African jungle! Deedee and
Bouncer liked their winter home.
There they could see their friends
Cheeky Chimpanzee and Polly Parrot
from time to time.

16 October

Cheeky and Polly

The winter home was a lively place. Hundreds of colourful birds
twittered and chirped from the branches of the tropical trees.
Chimpanzees swung from tree to tree.
The elephants were much quieter; they ambled through their part of
the winter home quite calmly. Deedee was standing by the fence.
"Hey Cheeky!" she called out.
"Hello Deedee!" answered the chimpanzee. He swung over to Deedee
in no time, followed by a lovely crested parrot.
"Polly. You're here too!" cried Deedee.
A little later, Polly flew over to the elephants clutching a banana in her beak.
It was a welcoming present from Cheeky to Deedee. Polly was very
happy to see her elephant friends again too. They would be
able to play together through the winter.

17 October

Good friends

When we are together,
Everything is fine,
We laugh and joke, we chase and fight,
But the days always turn out right,
Because we're such good friends.

We have such fun together,
Everything is great,
We sing and dance, we play and run,
No matter what, we still have fun,
Because we're such good friends.

18 October

Let me out!

The elephants had got used to their winter home. Father and Mother were enjoying the rest. It was just like a holiday. They could sleep in in the mornings, go for a short walk, play a game for a while, eat a banana or two and then go back to bed. Deedee was bored. "I wish I could get out of here," she said to Bouncer, her little brother. "I'd like to get some fresh air." "Why don't you ask if you're allowed to?" suggested Bouncer. "I'd like to go with you." That evening they talked to Kevin. To their surprise, he agreed to let them out. "Tomorrow morning, before the visitors arrive, then you can go out for a while," he said.

192

19 October

Visiting Cheeky

Kevin kept his promise. That
morning, Deedee and Bouncer
were allowed to walk about freely.
They could visit their friend Cheeky
Chimpanzee. Both Deedee and
Bouncer took a few shiny apples
with them as a present for
Cheeky. They walked over to
the chimpanzee's cage.
"Yoohoo!" called Deedee.
"Cheeky, we've got a surprise
for you!"
Cheeky had only just woken up.
He couldn't believe his eyes.
"Am I dreaming? Is that you?"
he asked in amazement.
He gave his shiny brown
eyes a jolly good rub.
"Good morning!"
called out Deedee and
Bouncer. "We've come
to visit you!"

20 October

Breakfast
together

"We have to be
back in the elephant
park before the visitors
arrive," said Deedee.
"How nice of you to come!" said Cheeky. He felt wide awake. "And you've brought me
such delicious apples. I've got some bananas here. Shall we have breakfast together?"
So the friends sat down round a tree stump and munched their bananas and apples.
"We should do this more often," said Cheeky. "It's so nice to have company for
breakfast."

21 October

Too late!

Cheeky made a hat out of a banana skin. He put it on his head and pulled funny faces. Deedee and Bouncer laughed so much that their tummies began to hurt. Then they heard voices, but not animal voices, human voices. "Look at that!" said a small girl. "Two elephants in the chimpanzee's cage!"

"Oh no!" cried Deedee. "We're really late! We were supposed to be home before the visitors arrived."

"I hope Kevin won't be cross," whispered Bouncer. He was afraid that they wouldn't be allowed to visit Cheeky again because they weren't back home on time.

The missing children

Father, Mother and Uncle Jumbo
had just woken up. It was nearly nine
o'clock. They enjoyed their long lie-ins
during the winter months. There was no
need to get up early, as long as they were
up in time for the visitors.
"What a lovely sleep," yawned Father.
"What's happened?" cried Mother. "Where are the children?"
They were really worried. Their children had gone and
the door to their quarters was locked.

Nowhere to be found

"I don't understand," muttered Uncle Jumbo. "They're
always waiting for me to tell them a joke in the mornings."
The grown-up elephants searched again, but Deedee
and Bouncer were nowhere to be found. Poor Mother
began to cry.
"Perhaps they've been gone all night and we didn't even
know," she sniffed. "How did they leave without us
hearing something? Father, you're sure you didn't hear
anything?" He shook his head with dismay.
"It's as if we dreamt them away," he said. "I don't
understand what could have happened."

24 October

Away from home

Deedee and Bouncer were having such a lovely breakfast that they had completely forgotten the time. They would have to rush back to the elephant home. Deedee was very upset.
"I promised faithfully that we'd be back on time," she moaned.
"Kevin will feel we have let him down."
The visitors were amused to see two elephants in a chimpanzee's cage. The door of the cage was slightly open, so Deedee and Bouncer crept out as quietly as they could. But the visitors couldn't take their eyes off them.

25 October

A stroke and a pat

"Oh, mother!" cried out a young girl. "Please may I stroke that little elephant?" "Look!" called out a little boy too. "Aren't they lovely elephants? Let's get a little bit closer." A crowd gathered round. They were thrilled to be so close to the elephants. Deedee and Bouncer couldn't get through. The people stroked and patted the elephants and took photograhs. They really were the centre of attention.

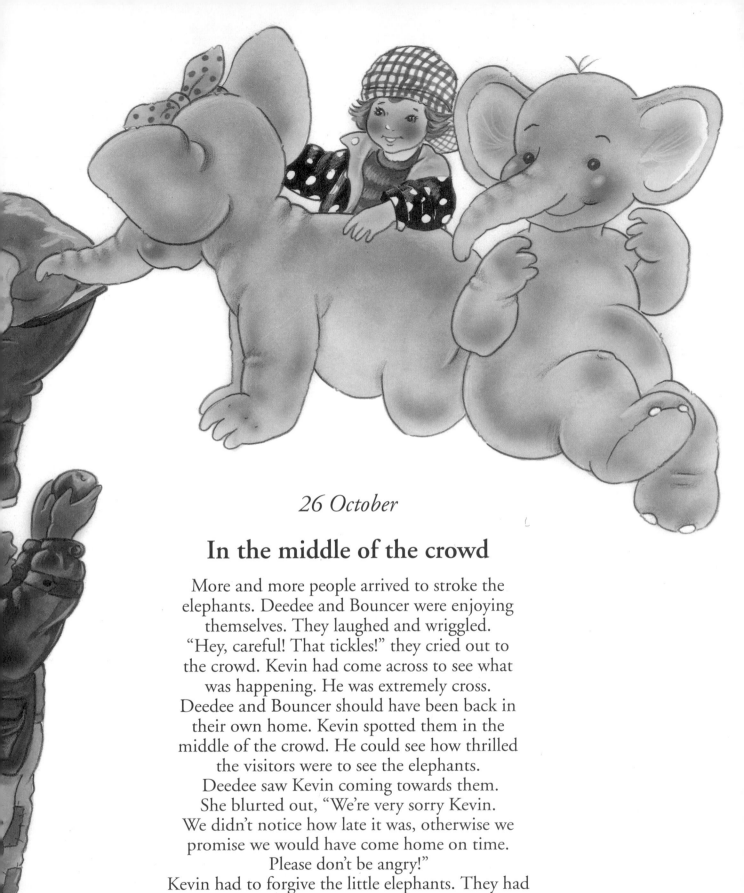

26 October

In the middle of the crowd

More and more people arrived to stroke the
elephants. Deedee and Bouncer were enjoying
themselves. They laughed and wriggled.
"Hey, careful! That tickles!" they cried out to
the crowd. Kevin had come across to see what
was happening. He was extremely cross.
Deedee and Bouncer should have been back in
their own home. Kevin spotted them in the
middle of the crowd. He could see how thrilled
the visitors were to see the elephants.
Deedee saw Kevin coming towards them.
She blurted out, "We're very sorry Kevin.
We didn't notice how late it was, otherwise we
promise we would have come home on time.
Please don't be angry!"
Kevin had to forgive the little elephants. They had
just got over-excited. "Come on, you two," he said
with a smile. "Time to take you home."

197

27 October

A beautiful autumn day

Kevin was walking round the zoo early
one morning. All the animals were asleep.
The mist thinned and the sun started to glisten.
Day was breaking. The cool, fresh autumn
air made his nose glow. He walked through
the fallen leaves. Crunch, crunch, crunch!
Kevin decided that the elephants should
go outside for the day. A trunkful of clean,
fresh autumn air would do
them good.

28 October

Out for the day

Whistling merrily, Kevin strolled
over to the elephants. Father, Mother
and Uncle Jumbo were waking up.
They yawned, grunted and stretched
their tired legs. Deedee and Bouncer
were already up and were feeling
lively. They shouted to their parents
to hurry up. "Do be quiet!"
grumbled Uncle Jumbo. "Let me
wake up properly first," yawned
Mother. "Morning Kevin," shouted
Deedee and Bouncer. As soon as
Kevin arrived, their day could start.
"Good morning everybody," replied
Kevin with a big smile on his face.
"It is a beautiful autumn day. The air
is fresh and cool and I think you
should go out for the day."

Looking for beech nuts

Kevin was right. It was a beautiful morning. The sun had risen and the trees and grass were crisp and bright. The spiders' webs glittered in the sunshine and the leaves on the trees were glorious shades of red and yellow. Deedee and Bouncer thought everything looked lovely.
Then Bouncer trod on something hard and prickly. "Ow!" he cried. "What is it?"
"It's a beech nut," explained Kevin. "It comes from that old beech tree. Beech nuts taste lovely, try one!"
Deedee and Bouncer rooted around under the leaves with their trunks, looking for beech nuts. They found lots and piled them up in a large heap. They did taste lovely.
"I want to look for beech nuts all day long," sighed Deedee.

30 October

Building plot

The fresh air and exercise were doing wonders for the elephants. "Now you can see what your beautiful new summer park looks like," said Kevin. They made their way to the site of their old summer park. But it had disappeared! Instead, all they could see were piles of earth, deep holes and heaps of stones. "Oh dear, whatever has happened to our park?" cried Mother. "Don't worry," replied Kevin. "I'll explain how it's going to look. They're putting the lake where that deep hole is, and that hump over there will be Uncle Jumbo's rocky hill." The elephants started to imagine what the park would look like. They were sure that when Spring came, they would have the most beautiful park in the world.

31 October

Deedee, the talking elephant

I'm Deedee, the talking elephant,
I'm good at chatter you see,
I can talk all day long hardly taking a breath,
I can talk, I can talk, I can talk you to death,
But not if I like you, not me.

I'm Deedee, the talking elephant,
I'll make conversation all day,
I can talk without thinking, I might not be clever,
Sometimes I can talk utter rubbish for ever,
But not if I like you, no way.

1 November

Knitting

Grandma Johnson had been busy for weeks.
Knitting. Her knitting needles clicked away.
She was knitting a surprise for her grandson,
Jonathan Johnson. She had started by collecting
lots of odd bits of wool, the more colours the better.
She had found a pattern for knitting cuddly toys
in a magazine. There were four different toys – a
dog, a cat, a rabbit and … an elephant! Grandma
Johnson knew straightaway which one to choose –
the elephant with the long trunk. She had almost
finished knitting it. Then, as soon as she had
stuffed it, the elephant would be ready.

2 November

Spiky hair

The cuddly elephant was finished. He looked
so colourful! But Grandma wasn't quite satisfied.
She wondered what was wrong. Then she realised.
There was still a little wool left, some green,
blue and yellow. So she made a pompom and
sewed the pompom on the top of the elephant's
head. It did look funny! An elephant with spiky
hair. All she had to do now was wrap up the
elephant, and the surprise present for Jonathan
was ready.

The surprise

Jonathan was very excited. His Grandma was coming to see them, and when she came, she usually brought him something. Grandma rung the bell. Jonathan ran to open the front door. "Hello Grandma, have you brought me anything?" asked Jonathan. "Shame on you Jonathan," said his mother crossly. "You shouldn't ask for presents. That's very rude and greedy." But Grandma laughed and patted his head. She pulled out a parcel from her bag. Jonathan ripped off the paper. "Oh Grandma, an elephant. It's lovely. Thank you so much."

4 November

A name

When Jonathan went to bed, he took the elephant with him. "Have you given him a name yet?" asked his mother when she kissed him goodnight. "No, I haven't!" said Jonathan. He had been thinking about a name, but he just couldn't think of the right name. Finally he got to sleep, but he tossed and turned all night and pushed his new elephant out of bed. Plop, right into one of Jonathan's slippers.

5 November

Disappeared

Sunlight streamed through Jonathan's window. He woke up. The first thing he remembered was his cuddly elephant from his Grandma, but he couldn't find it. Jonathan searched his bed. He thought it was strange how the elephant had just disappeared. It wasn't under the duvet, or under his pillow. "Mother!" shouted Jonathan. "My elephant has gone!" His mother came in and laughed. "Jonathan, just look what's in your slipper!" He was so relieved he hadn't lost him for good.

6 November

Slipper

As Jonathan reached down to grab his elephant from his slipper, he suddenly had an idea. "I know what I can call you. I'm going to call you Slipper the elephant," he said to his new friend. "Not just because you fell into my slipper, but also because you're just as warm and soft as my slippers." It looked like the elephant winked! He must have been happy with his new name.

7 November

Tag

Jonathan had gone to school.
Slipper the elephant was lying on
Jonathan's bed and was feeling rather
bored. Then he heard a noise. It came
from the toy corner. Slipper slid off
the bed and went to have a look.
"Hey, what are you doing?"
he asked a teddy bear.
"We're playing tag and hide-and-seek,"
answered Teddy.
"May I play too?" Slipper asked.
Teddy thought for a moment.
"All right then," he said, "we're
playing tag and you're it."

8 November

Trunk

The teddy bear, the gnome and
all the other toys were running
round the room. Slipper was trying
to catch one of them. He chased the
gnome, but he was too quick
for Slipper. So he chased Teddy.
He was trying so hard to catch
him that he tripped over his
own trunk. He landed in a heap.
The other toys laughed at him.
"Ha ha! Slipper the clumsy elephant!"
they cried.

206

9 November

Jealous

Slipper was feeling a bit upset. The other toys had laughed at him because he wasn't very good at running and he kept tripping over his trunk. With tears in his eyes, he crept to the corner. When Jonathan went up to bed later that evening, he looked for Slipper. "Where's Slipper?" he asked. "I need him. I won't be able to sleep without him. What's he doing over here?" Jonathan picked up Slipper from the corner and got into bed. Peeping over the edge of the duvet, Slipper could just see the toy corner. All the other toys were jealous. Teddy and Gnome would have loved to be under the nice warm duvet instead of being crammed in the toy corner. Slipper felt a lot happier; he felt proud that he had been chosen by Jonathan.

10 November

Whistling toes

Slipper might have been a bit slow and clumsy, but there was one thing he was very good at. He was very good indeed at whistling on his toes.
Lots of people could whistle on their fingers, but almost nobody could whistle on their toes. You need a trunk to whistle on your toes. Otherwise you can't reach. Slipper's trunk was long enough and, when he was in the mood, he rolled over on to his back, got hold of one of his feet with his trunk and whistled a happy tune.

11 November

Toe music

Slipper the elephant loves to play music,
The clarinet, trumpet and cello,
With violin and bow, he puts on a good show,
He's really a musical fellow.

But sometimes he stretches his long woolly trunk,
And breathes a huge lungful of air,
He blows on his toes, out through his great nose,
And whistles with such great flair.

12 November

Orchestra

Slipper was lying on the bed, whistling as loud as he could on his toes. It cheered up all the other toys. Teddy leapt up. He had had an idea. He picked up one of Jonathan's toy drums and started to bang it. The gnome heard him and decided to join in. He found a xylophone and two sticks. It sounded like a little orchestra. They needed to practise a bit at first, but they quickly got the hang of it, and they sounded quite good. Even some of Jonathan's cars joined in, rolling backwards and forwards in time with the music.

209

13 November

Feeling sick

"Yuck," said Slipper to himself, "I don't feel at all well. I feel really sick."
He tried to stand up, but he couldn't. His legs were all floppy. Slipper
looked down at his tummy and jumped back with fright. There was
a great big hole there. All the stuffing was coming out through
the hole.
"Help," cried Slipper, frightened. "I'm falling apart. Help!"

14 November

Help!

Why was Slipper's stuffing coming out through a hole in his tummy?
What had happened? Perhaps Grandma hadn't tied a proper knot in
the end of the wool when she sewed up Slipper. Slipper lay in a floppy,
flat heap on Jonathan's bed. The only lively thing about him was his
pompom of hair. Jonathan would get a big shock when he saw Slipper.

15 November

The dolls' hospital

When Jonathan got home from school, he went to
his room and saw Slipper lying there on the bed.
Flat and floppy. Next to him was a pile of stuffing.
Jonathan was shocked, but he quickly realised what had
happened. He grabbed Slipper and ran to his mother.
Luckily his mother knew exactly what to do.
"We'll take Slipper to the dolls' hospital
The doctor there will be able to fix him."
"Are you quite sure?" asked Jonathan.
"Absolutely!" laughed his mother. "Doctor Button
is a very clever dolls' doctor."

16 November

Sticking plaster

Mr Button, the dolls' doctor, gave
Slipper a thorough examination.
"I must be sure," he said, "that there
aren't any more holes. Otherwise I'll
have to stuff him all over again another
day." Slipper was fat and round again
and stood proudly on Jonathan's bed.
Doctor Button had stuck a large sticking
plaster on his tummy. The other toys
stared at the plaster with amazement.
"Did it hurt?" they wanted to know.
"Oh, it wasn't too bad," answered Slipper
bravely. The toys thought he was such
a hero. They didn't feel like
teasing him anymore.

17 November

Winter jumper

It's getting much colder outside now,
With an icy and wintry blast,
Jonathan needs a new jumper,
Could Grandma knit one fast?

So Grandma says yes she could knit one,
Her needles click fast through the night,
And from all the small pieces left over,
She knits one for Slipper, it's just right.

18 November

Pedal-car

"Come on Slipper," called Jonathan. "I'm going for a walk. If you want to come too, I'll pull you along in my cart."
That sounded like fun to Slipper. He had never been outside to play.
"Wait," said Jonathan. "We'd better put on our new winter jumpers first. They will keep us warm."
A few minutes later, Slipper was sitting in the cart in his nice warm jumper. The sun was shining and the birds were singing. He was really enjoying himself.

19 November

The hole

Jonathan started to run faster and faster. Whooosh!
The wind whistled past Slipper's ears. Slipper was excited,
but he was a little bit frightened too. Jonathan was
running faster and faster, so fast that he didn't notice
a hole in the road. The cart hit the hole with a loud
bump and up flew Slipper and then down,
down to the ground.
"Help! Help! Don't leave me here!" shouted Slipper,
but Jonathan hadn't seen the hole and he
carried on running.

20 November

Afraid

Slipper had been lying at the side of the road,
but he had no idea for how long.
It was getting dark, and Slipper felt lonely and
forgotten. He began to cry. Then he heard
Jonathan's voice. "Look! There's Slipper!"
Slipper felt so relieved that he had been found and
he could go home. Jonathan had been so worried
when he discovered that Slipper wasn't in
the cart. He had gone out again with his
father to search for him.

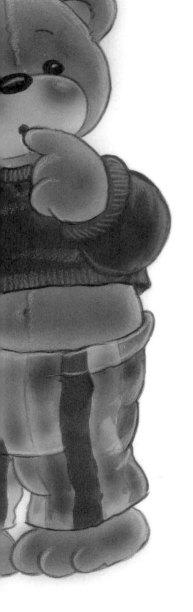

21 November

Visitors

Ellen, Jonathan's cousin, had come
to stay for a few days. She was rather
spoiled and had a lot of very expensive
toys. All these toys had to stay in
Jonathan's room.
Slipper was curious and went to have a
closer look at all these visiting toys.
"Hello, I'm Slipper," he said, being
friendly. The expensive toys didn't answer.
Jonathan's teddy bear knew all about
them. "Don't bother with them," he said.
"Those arrogant things don't want to
know us!"

22 November

The expensive toys

Slipper just didn't understand.
Why wouldn't Ellen's toys play
with him? There was only one thing
to do, he thought, he would have to
go and ask them.
He marched over to an expensive toy
pram and asked, "Why don't you want
to play with me?"
"Me? Play with a dirty old cuddly toy
made out of leftover bits of wool?
I wouldn't dream of it!" said the pram.
Slipper couldn't believe his ears. "What
an awful thing to say," he thought.

23 November

Whispers

Slipper was sitting on the bed watching Ellen's expensive toys. He glared at the arrogant pram and all the dolls. They were standing in a corner. They had been standing there for ages, because Ellen hadn't played with them once since she had arrived.
"Perhaps that's why her toys aren't very friendly or nice," said Slipper to himself. "I think I'll whisper something in Jonathan's ear tonight."
When Jonathan was asleep, Slipper whispered very softly in his ear, "Perhaps you and Ellen could play with the dolls tomorrow?"

24 November

Mothers and fathers

"Guess what I dreamed about last night?" Jonathan asked Ellen. "That we were playing mothers and fathers."
"What a good idea!" cried Ellen. "My dolls can be the children and we'll take them out in the pram."
"Great," said Jonathan, "but Slipper the elephant should come too. He can be our pet."
Half and hour later, Slipper was sitting in the pram with all the dolls. The little outing had cheered up the lonely dolls and they found that they were having a great time with Slipper.

25 November

In the middle of the night

It was the middle of the night, but Teddy and Gnome were not asleep. They had got a plan. They were going on an adventure that night. Jonathan's bedroom door had been left open, so they could explore the whole house. Discussing their plan, they managed to wake Slipper.
"What are you two up to?" he whispered.
"We're going to explore the house. Are you coming?" they asked.
"You bet!" answered Slipper.
Carefully, he slid out of bed and crept along behind Teddy and Gnome as they tip-toed out of the door. It was very dark in the house. All the lights had been switched off. The three friends soon got tired of their adventures.
"I'm going back!" muttered Teddy. "I can't see a thing."
"We're coming with you," said the other two. "It's much nicer in Jonathan's room than in a cold, dark house."

A draught

Teddy, Gnome and Slipper crept along the landing.
"Brrr," shivered Slipper, "it's so cold here."
"I agree," answered Teddy, "there's a draught.
I think the window in Jonathan's bedroom is still
open." The words were hardly out of his mouth
when Jonathan's bedroom door blew shut from
the draught. Their mouths dropped open.
They were stuck on the landing. How were
they going to get back into the bedroom?

27 November

Stuck!

Slipper thought hard about how to get back into the
bedroom. They had to do it before Jonathan woke up.
He had an idea. "Gnome, you climb on to Teddy's
shoulders. Then I'll climb on to your shoulders and
try to pull the handle."
Teddy muttered, "Why do we have to be at the bottom
and you on top? That's not fair!"
"Perhaps, but it is sensible," replied Slipper,
"because I've got a long trunk and I think I can just
reach the handle with it."

28 November

Grubby

Slipper was no longer a new toy. He had got a bit threadbare and worn, and certainly a bit grubby. But Jonathan couldn't sleep without him, not even for one night.
"I can't sleep without Slipper!" he cried, when his mother tried to wash Slipper.
She understood, of course, but she thought Slipper was long overdue for a wash. His trunk was the worst bit, because Jonathan chewed it in bed at night.

29 November

In the washing machine

As soon as Jonathan had left for school, his mother went upstairs to strip his bed. The sheets and pillowcases needed washing. Into the washing machine they went. But where was Slipper? He wasn't in Jonathan's room. Where had he got to? When Jonathan's mother emptied the machine an hour later, there was a lump in one of the pillowcases. Surely Slipper wasn't in the washing machine, was he? Oh dear, yes he was! He was soaking wet. Luckily, the sun was shining, so Mother hung him out to dry on the washing line. She hoped he would be dry before Jonathan came home from school.

30 November

On the washing line

Poor Slipper is practically dry now,
He was put in the washing machine.
Mother, stripping the bed, didn't see him,
So now he's amazingly clean.

He's pegged to the line with two ear pegs,
And feeling quite foolish and shy,
But the sun is still shining so brightly
That soon he'll be perfectly dry.

1 December

Blue-eyed Bunter

To look at Bunter, you wouldn't think there was anything particularly special about him. Bunter was just an ordinary boy elephant, grey, with a big, round tummy, four chunky legs and a long trunk.

But there was something unusual about Bunter. It was his eyes. They were sky blue. Elephants normally have brown eye, but not Bunter. His eyes were like two clear pools.

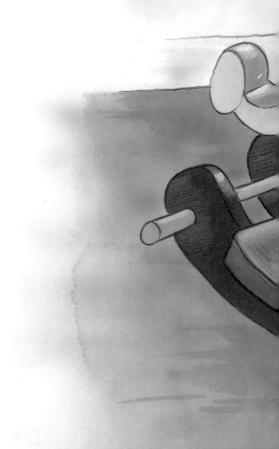

2 December

Little angel

When Bunter was born and he opened his eyes for the first time, all his aunts oohed and aahed. "What beautiful blue eyes!" said Aunt Alice, "he's bound to be a sweet child. A little angel." Aunt Alice found out soon enough that she was quite wrong. As soon as he could walk, Bunter began to be naughty, getting up to mischief all the time.
"Well, I was mistaken," sighed Aunt Alice, "he's not a little angel, he's a little terror!"

3 December

Mischief

Little Bunter Elephant
Is not quite what he seems,
For underneath that angel face,
He's full of naughty schemes.

Every day from morn till night,
Come rain, come shine, come hail,
It's mischief, mischief all the way,
It's mischief without fail.

4 December

Sigh

Bunter's mother let out a great sigh.
"What am I going to do with that boy? A day
doesn't go by without him getting up to something.
The day before yesterday he was trying to jump over
the stream and he fell into the mud. Yesterday I
found a frog in my bed. Now, I wonder who put it
there?" Bunter's father tried not to laugh. He was
quite amused by Bunter's exploits. So that
was where Bunter got his mischievous
streak from. Like father, like son!

222

5 December

Sledging

After school, Bunter and his friends walked home together. It had been snowing. They rolled in the snow and threw snowballs at each other. Not far from school was a small hill that was covered in a thick layer of snow. "Look! What an excellent slide. What a shame we haven't got our sledges," cried Bunter. Then he had an idea. He walked up to the top of the hill, put his school bag on the ground, sat on it and slid down to the bottom. "It makes a brilliant sledge!" he shouted to his friends.

6 December

Soggy books

Bunter got home very late. "Where have you been? I've been worried about you," asked his mother. "Oh, I've been sledging with my friends," replied Bunter. "Where did you get the sledge from?" His mother was curious. "We had it with us," said Bunter, "It was a very unusual sledge. I used my school bag." Bunter's mother was extremely angry. She opened his school bag to find a pile of soggy schoolbooks.

223

7 December

Exciting plans

Bunter the blue-eyed elephant was a happy young elephant. He always made time to think up exciting plans. So all the boys in his class wanted to be his friend.

"Hey Bunter, what shall we do this afternoon?" his friends asked.

Bunter stroked his trunk and considered what they could do. Then he said, "I know. Let's form a secret club. A pirate club."

8 December

The pirate club

Bunter, of course, was the chief pirate. Only real pirates were allowed to join the secret pirate club. But how did anyone become a real pirate?

To begin with, they had to look like a real pirate. Bunter had searched through his mother's wardrobe for useful pirate clothes. He found a lovely red scarf with white polka dots and he tied it round his head. He also found a golden belt from his mother's party dress. He fastened it round his big tummy and then stuck his toy sword through it. Now, he looked more like a pirate. His mother wouldn't be too pleased with his costume though!

9 December

An eyepatch

Bunter the elephant was sitting with the other pirates in the secret hut. Chief Pirate Bunter inspected the other pirates. They all looked the part – mean and dangerous. All of them had tied scarves round their heads and belts round their middles. But Bunter knew that something was missing.

"I've got it!" he yelled. "A real pirate has an eyepatch!" "Yes, you're right Bunter," agreed the others, "but where are we going to eyepatches? We can't ask at home, because then the club wouldn't be secret anymore. They'd be bound to ask us what we needed eyepatches for."

10 December

Caught!

Very quietly, Bunter crept into his house. He needed to find eyepatches for the members of the secret pirate club, but he couldn't just ask for them, because the club had to remain a secret.

He was sure that there would be pieces of material and elastic in his mother's sewing basket. Carefully, he opened it...

"What are you up to Bunter?" Bunter jumped back with fright. There was his mother, and she looked very cross. Bunter suddenly remembered that he was wearing his pirate clothes – his mother's red scarf and gold belt!

11 December

Punishment

Mother elephant was really very angry with Bunter after this last episode. Even Bunter's father thought that enough was enough. "Bunter," said his mother, "we've had quite enough of all this mischief. So you're going to be punished. You may not go out to play for a week."
"Yes, but ..." stammered Bunter.
"No buts. You cannot go out for a week. No arguing," shouted his father.
Bunter shuffled off sadly to his bedroom. "A whole week indoors! What a terrible punishment," he thought. He promised himself that he would be better behaved in the future.

12 December

The window

Bunter looked outside. It was a lovely day and he wasn't allowed out to play. He could see his friends playing with a ball. Bunter jumped up excitedly. He had an idea. He opened the window and shouted to his friends, "Hey, throw the ball to me. I might not be able to play outside, but I can still play inside!"
His friends laughed and threw the ball to Bunter. But they didn't aim very well and ... crash! Bunter's bedroom window shattered. Bunter's idea wasn't very clever after all.

13 December

Sorrow

Big tears rolled down Bunter's trunk. He had been told off again, and he was still being punished for last week's naughtiness. "But Mother," he sniffed, "I don't do it on purpose. Things just seem to go wrong all by themselves." His mother gave him a little smile. "There's mischief in your bones," she sighed. "But do try to be good, just for one day, eh Bunter?" Bunter promised to do his best.

14 December

Home alone

It was a miracle! Bunter hadn't done anything naughty all day. "You see Bunter, you can do it if you try," said his mother. "So I'm going to let you stay at home on your own this evening because father and I have to go out for a little while." So Bunter was left in the house alone. The television was on and his mother had left him a glass of cola and a packet of peanuts. "Go to bed at seven o'clock, and look after the house!" she said. Bunter was having a whale of a time. He finished the cola and peanuts very quickly. He wondered what time it was and looked at the clock. Half past six. Half an hour to go. But when Father and Mother got home, they found Bunter fast asleep on the sofa. "Some house-sitter!" laughed his father.

15 December

A new sweet shop

"Bunter, are you coming with us after school?" asked the other children in his class. "There's a new sweet shop in the village. It's opening today. They're giving all the children a free lollipop."
"Do you need to ask! Of course I'm coming," chuckled Bunter. After school, they all walked to the village together. But they weren't the only ones. What a crowd! It looked like the whole world wanted a free lollipop.
"I don't feel like waiting in a queue," moaned Bunter.
Bunter had to try to be patient.

16 December

Tricked

Bunter and his friends were standing in a queue at the front of the sweet shop. But it was incredibly busy at the new shop. They probably would have to stand in the queue for hours. Bunter had an idea.
"Just copy me," he told his friends.
He walked away from the shop, jumped up and down and pointed, "Oh look! Look over there!"
Everyone in the queue looked up. They wondered what Bunter had seen. While all the people were looking the other way, Bunter and his friends sneaked quickly into the shop.

Heart of gold

"I think sweets are the must delicious things in the world,"
sighed Bunter. He clutched a large lollipop in his trunk.
On the way home, they passed their friend
Tubby's house. Tubby loved sweet things
too, but he wasn't feeling well.
"I feel sorry for Tubby," Bunter thought.
"I'll give him my lollipop. I'm sure
he'll eat it when he feels better."
Bunter may have been a mischievous
elephant, but he had a heart of gold.

18 December

Hundreds and hundreds

Do you like chocolate and toffees?
Wine gums, liquorice too?
I could eat hundreds and hundreds,
But then I am me and not you.

But if you're unhappy or poorly,
And have to stay tucked up in bed,
Don't cry if the medicine's nasty,
You can have all my chocolate instead.

229

19 December

Gone fishing

"Mother, where's my fishing rod?" called out Bunter.
"Your fishing rod?" asked his mother in amazement.
"Bunter, it's freezing outside. The lake will be solid ice.
You can't possibly go fishing."
"Oh yes I can," insisted Bunter. "Fred's father has
made a hole in the ice. All we have to do is drop our
lines into the hole and the fish will bite."
"Are you sure?" said his mother anxiously.
"Be careful, won't you Bunter?"

20 December

Big, grey fish

Bunter and Fred had only been gone
about fifteen minutes when the telephone
rang at Bunter's house. It was Fred's mother.
"Good morning, Mrs Elephant," she said.
"I've got two big, grey fish here.
My husband fished them out of the water."
Bunter's mother knew immediately
what had happened. Bunter and Fred
had fallen through the ice. So, instead
of catching fish, they had to be fished
out of the water themselves!

230

21 December

A bad cold

Bunter Elephant had a fever. When he and Fred had fallen through the ice, the water was absolutely freezing. Mother put him straight to bed, but it was too late. Bunter had caught a bad cold. His mother was quite worried about him and came to check on him every half-hour. But she was relieved to discover that his temperature had fallen. "It's hard work looking after a sick child," she sighed. "But there is one advantage. When Bunter is ill, he can't get up to any mischief!"

22 December

Stay inside

"Please may I go outside Mother?" pleaded Bunter.
"No, you must stay inside today," she replied firmly.
"Have I been naughty?" Bunter asked.
"Not as far as I know," sighed his mother, "but you must stay inside today because you had a fever yesterday."
"That's not fair," moaned Bunter. "I'm better now!"
He had slept such a lot the day before that he had twice as much energy that day. When his mother saw that mischievous look in Bunter's blue eyes, she was glad she had a reason to keep him indoors.

231

23 December

The Christmas Fair

Bunter's mother had been making little cakes all week. She was going to sell them that evening at the Christmas Fair. All the money they collected was to go to charity. That year the money would help poor elephants in Africa, who were starving.

Bunter had to go with his mother to the Christmas Fair. He was going to help sell the cakes.

"I don't want to go," he moaned. "Why do I have to go?"

"Because it's Christmas," said his mother.

24 December

Helping

Mother saw the puzzled look on Bunter's face and explained, "Christmas is a time of peace and happiness. But there are still lots of poor animals who have no food to eat and no homes to go to. It's not a very happy Christmas for them. That's why we must try to help them by selling our cakes and giving them the money. Do you understand now Bunter?"

Bunter felt a little bit guilty for not thinking of the animals who had no food to eat. He understood how terrible it must be for them. He was determined to work his hardest and sell as many cakes as he could.

Greedy Bunter

Bunter had a customer. "There you are sir, one bagful of cakes. One pound fifty please," said Bunter politely. The man took the bag and looked inside. With a look of utter amazement, he took one of the cakes out of the bag. Someone had taken a bite out of it. Bunter blushed. Looking at the cakes had made him so hungry that he had taken a little nibble! Bunter felt ashamed. He couldn't sell cakes like that. He might as well have eaten all the cake himself. Bunter was a bit silly to think that people would be happy to eat cakes with big bites taken out of them!

Sleigh

Christmas is a festive time,
Be happy one and all,
Santa Claus brings presents
To children big and small.

He flies over the countryside,
By night, but not by day,
He piles up all the presents
On his reindeer-driven sleigh!

27 December

Let's play Santa Claus

Bunter loved Christmas. He especially loved the Christmas tree with all the decorations and lights. He had thought up a new game with his friend Fred. They were going to play Santa Claus. They had decorated Bunter's sledge with fir branches. Bunter just happened to have a red hat, so he would be Santa Claus. Fred stuck a branch behind each ear and said with a chuckle, "I'm the reindeer."

28 December

Naughty Santa Claus

Bunter and Fred set off through the village. Santa Bunter should have had presents for everyone. Do you think he did? His eyes shone with mischief as he arrived at Tubby's house. "Hey, Tubby!" he shouted. "I'm Santa Claus and I've got something for you!" Tubby rushed outside. What was Santa Bunter going to give him? He certainly did get something from Bunter. A snowball right in his face! "You're a naughty Santa Claus!" shouted Tubby as Bunter, Fred and the sledge disappeared round the corner.

235

29 December

The skating rink

IIt had been really cold weather all week.
The lake in the park was frozen.
"Mother, I'm going to the park,"
said Bunter. "There's an ice-skating
rink and music too."
"That's fine Bunter," said his mother,
"but do be careful on the ice."
Bunter smiled and said, "Oh, there
won't be any problems this time.
Don't worry!"
Later, when his mother looked in the
cupboard, she saw Bunter's skates.
She wondered what Bunter was up
to in the park.

30 December

Mince pies

For two days Bunter had been skating,
but without his skates! His mother was
puzzled. What had Bunter been doing
in the park for two days? She was amazed
when he came home that evening with
a huge bag of mince pies.
Bunter laughed, "Don't look so surprised!
I earned the mince pies myself. I kept
the rink nice and clean for the others by
blowing all the twigs and snow off with
my trunk. They gave me these mince pies
to say thank you. So now we can have
them with our tea!"

31 December

Happy New Year!

Whatever else will happen
On the last day of the year,
I'm going to have a party,
And give a great big cheer!

I'm staying up so very late,
I'll eat too much I fear,
But that won't stop me wishing you
"A Hap-Hap-Happy New Year!"